Super Duper® Publications

Webber®
Core Curriculum
Vocabulary Cards
Fun Sheets

Level One

Research-Based
Worksheets

Written & Illustrated by the Super Duper® Staff

Printed in the United States

ISBN 978-1060723-040-3

Super Duper® Publications
www.superduperinc.com
Post Office Box 24997 • Greenville, SC 29616 USA
1-800-277-8737 • Fax 1-800-978-7379

Introduction

Webber® Core Curriculum Vocabulary Cards Fun Sheets – Level One doubles the opportunities for teaching vocabulary available in the original *Webber® Core Curriculum Vocabulary Cards*! This reproducible companion workbook has 104 pages of activities to help teach and reinforce the 100 research-based vocabulary words presented in the *Webber® Core Curriculum Cards – Level One*. Each subject area (Language Arts, Math, Science, and Social Studies) contains 25 core curriculum words students need to know in order to experience confidence and success in the classroom.

Each activity page helps students build confidence in their vocabulary skills, encourages following directions, and improves their comprehension of these basic, but critical, terms. Regular classroom teachers, speech-language pathologists, reading specialists, and special education teachers can use this book **with or without** the *Core Curriculum Cards* in one-on-one therapy sessions, with small groups, or with an entire class.

Each subject area provides activities that include

- Definition Matchup

- Vocabulary Comprehension

- WH Questions

- Vocabulary in Context

- Categories

- Phonological Awareness

- Spelling

- Writing Definitions

Webber® Core Curriculum Vocabulary Cards Fun Sheets – Level One is ideal for students in Title 1, ESL, or Head Start programs as well as students with special needs. Use the worksheets for extension activities, homework, or simple assessments.

Table of Contents

Parent/Helper Letter

Date: _____

Dear Parent/Helper:

Your child is currently working on _____ .

The attached worksheet(s) will help your child practice and reinforce skills reviewed in the classroom.

☐ After you complete these exercises with your child, please sign and return them by _____.

☐ Please complete these exercises with your child. You do not need to return them to me.

☐ _____

_____

_____

Thank you for your support.

_____   _____
Teacher/Speech-Language Pathologist   Parent/Helper Signature

Language Arts – Definitions Match-Up

Directions: Draw a line from the definition in Column A to the word that matches it in Column B. Read/Say the definition and its matching vocabulary word aloud.

A

Where do you live **?**
This is the punctuation mark at the end of a sentence that asks a question.

This is a person who draws pictures for a book.

English
Español
Português
This is how people talk with each other using words or signs.

a e i o u and sometimes **y**
These are the letters of the alphabet that are NOT consonants.

These are the steps that tell you how to do something.

These are the words you know.

B

vowels

language

question mark

vocabulary

illustrator

directions

Name   Date   Helper

Language Arts – Star Match-Up

Directions: Cut out the definitions at the bottom of the page. Shuffle the definitions and place them facedown. Have students take turns reading the definitions and placing them next to the correct pictures. The first player to find the star is the winner.

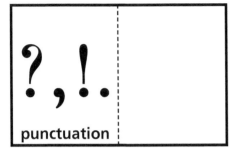

punctuation

predict

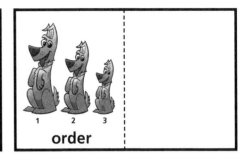

order

capitalize

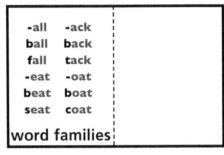

word families

middle

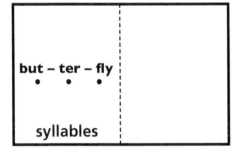

syllables

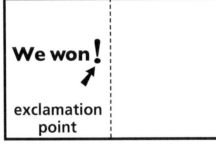

exclamation point

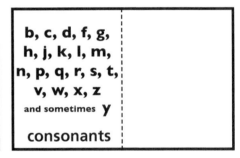

consonants

These are marks we use when we write sentences.	This is when you change a letter from lowercase to uppercase.	This is the punctuation mark at the end of a sentence that shows strong feeling.	This is the way you arrange things.	This is when you guess about what will happen.
	These are groups of words that end with the same letters and rhyme.	This word means someone or something that is in the center.	These are the letters of the alphabet that are NOT vowels.	These are the smaller parts of a word.

_____   _____   _____
Name   Date   Helper

#BKCRD-44 *Core Curriculum Vocab Cards Fun Sheets – Level 1* • ©2012 Super Duper® Publications • www.superduperinc.com

Language Arts – Treasure Chest Match-Up

Directions: Cut out the definitions at the bottom of the page. Shuffle the definitions and place them facedown. Have students take turns reading the definitions and placing them next to the correct pictures. The first player to find the treasure chest is the winner.

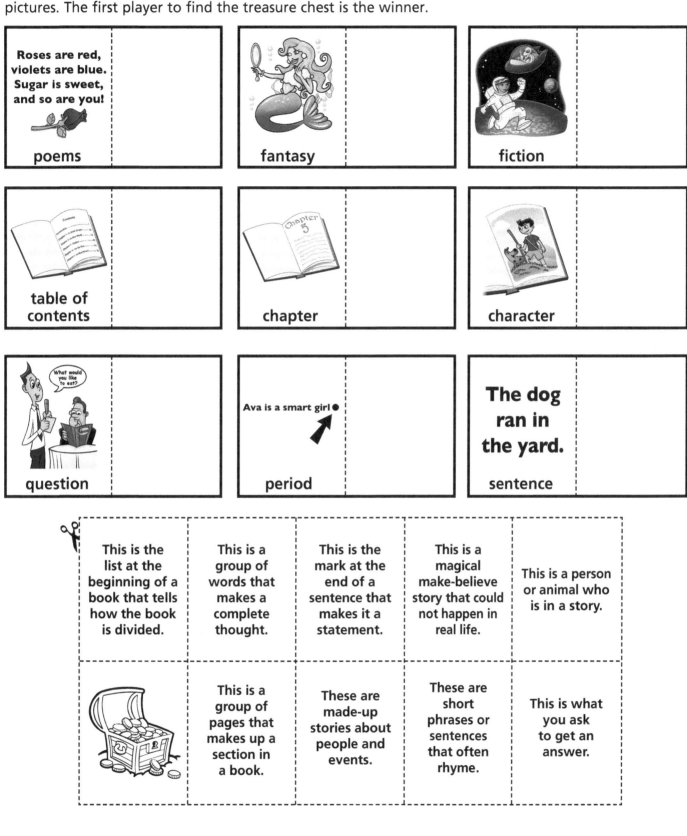

Language Arts – What's the Correct Meaning?

Directions: Read each sentence. Circle the picture and definition on the right that have the correct meaning for the word in bold.

1. Your sentences must have the correct **punctuation**.

These are marks we use when we write sentences.

-all   -ack
ball   back
fall   tack
-eat   -oat
beat   boat
seat   coat

These are groups of words that end with the same letters and rhyme.

---

2. Were you asking me a **question**?

These are the words you know.

This is what you ask to get an answer.

---

3. I stood in the **middle** of the group.

This is someone or something that is in the center.

This is a person or animal who is in a story.

---

4. Juan's native **language** is Spanish.

English
Español
Português

This is how people talk with each other using words or signs.

This is when you guess about what will happen.

---

5. It is hard to make words without **vowels**.

These are the steps that tell you how to do something.

a e i o u
and sometimes **y**

These are the letters of the alphabet that are NOT consonants.

---

6. All of my favorite books are **fiction**.

These are made-up stories about people and events.

The dog ran in the yard.

This is a group of words that makes a complete thought.

Name _____   Date _____   Helper _____

#BKCRD-44 Core Curriculum Vocab Cards Fun Sheets – Level 1 • ©2012 Super Duper® Publications • www.superduperinc.com

Language Arts – What's the Correct Meaning?

Directions: Read each sentence. Circle the picture and definition on the right that have the correct meaning for the word in bold.

1. Who is the main **character** in the story?

This is a person who draws pictures for a book.

This is a person or animal who is in a story.

---

2. How many **syllables** are in your name?

but – ter – fly
•   •   •
These are the smaller parts of a word.

This is a magical make-believe story that could not happen in real life.

---

3. Not counting "y," there are 20 **consonants**.

This is the list at the beginning of a book that tells how the book is divided into sections.

b, c, d, f, g, h, j, k, l, m, n, p, q, r, s, t, v, w, x, z
and sometimes y

These are the letters of the alphabet that are NOT vowels.

---

4. All statements end with a **period**.

Ava is a smart girl●

This is the mark at the end of a sentence that makes it a statement.

This is a group of pages that is in a book.

---

5. I like funny **poems** that rhyme.

English
Español
Português

This is how people talk with each other using words or signs.

Roses are red, violets are blue. Sugar is sweet, and so are you!

These are short phrases or sentences that often rhyme.

---

6. Who is the **author** of these mysteries?

This is a person who writes a story.

These are the words you know.

Name _____ Date _____ Helper _____

Language Arts – What's the Correct Meaning?

Directions: Read each sentence. Circle the picture and definition on the right that have the correct meaning for the word in bold.

1. The **table of contents** says the story is on page 72.

This is a person who draws pictures for a book.

This is the list at the beginning of a book that tells how the book is divided into sections.

2. A story about talking lions and flying pigs is a **fantasy**.

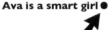

This is the mark at the end of a sentence that makes it a statement.

This is a magical make-believe story that could not happen in real life.

3. You must punctuate the end of a **sentence**.

The dog ran in the yard.

This is a group of words that makes a complete thought.

but – ter – fly
• • •

These are the smaller parts of a word.

4. None of us could **predict** the end of the story.

This is when you guess about what will happen.

English Español Português

This is how people talk with each other using words or signs.

5. Mom says I have a great **vocabulary** for a second grader.

This is when you change a letter from lowercase to uppercase.

These are the words you know.

6. Molly only read one **chapter** of her new book.

This is a group of pages that makes up a section in a book.

This word means someone or something that is in the center.

_____   _____   _____
Name   Date   Helper

#BKCRD-44 *Core Curriculum Vocab Cards Fun Sheets – Level 1* • ©2012 Super Duper® Publications • www.superduperinc.com

Language Arts – Answer It!

Directions: Read each question. Then, put an X on the letter next to the picture and vocabulary word that best answers the question.

1. What are groups of words that have the same ending sound?

   (A)
   language

   (B)
   word families

2. What do you do with the first letter of your name?

   (A)
   vowels

   (B)
   capitalize

3. What is the way you arrange things?

   (A)
   order

   (B)
   predict

4. Who draws pictures for books?

   (A)
   author

   (B)
   illustrator

5. What mark shows that a sentence has strong feeling?

   (A)
   exclamation point

   (B)
   period

6. What tells you how to do something?

   (A)
   table of contents

   (B)
   directions

_____ _____ _____
Name   Date   Helper

Language Arts – Answer It!

Directions: Read each question. Then, put an X on the letter next to the picture and vocabulary word that best answers the question.

1. Which letters are not consonants?

 a e i o u and sometimes **y**

vowels

 Roses are red, violets are blue. Sugar is sweet, and so are you!

poems

2. Which stories are about made-up people and events?

chapter

fiction

3. Where is the center?

order

middle

4. What do you ask someone to get an answer?

question

author

5. What comes after a question or statement?

 ? , ! .

punctuation

 b, c, d, f, g, h, j, k, l, m, n, p, q, r, s, t, v, w, x, z and sometimes **y**

consonants

6. What do all the words you know make up?

-all	-ack
ball	back
fall	tack
-eat	-oat
beat	boat
seat	coat

word families

vocabulary

_____   _____   _____
Name   Date   Helper

#BKCRD-44 Core Curriculum Vocab Cards Fun Sheets – Level 1 • ©2012 Super Duper® Publications • www.superduperinc.com

Language Arts – Answer It!

Directions: Read each question. Then, put an X on the letter next to the picture and vocabulary word that best answers the question.

1. What do you call a group of pages that make up a section in a book?

   (A) chapter

   (B) **a e i o u** and sometimes **y** vowels

---

2. What punctuation mark is at the end of a question?

   (A) **We won !** exclamation point

   (B)  Where do you live **?** question mark

---

3. What is a story that cannot happen in real life?

   (A) Roses are red, violets are blue. Sugar is sweet, and so are you! poems

   (B) fantasy

---

4. Which tells us how a book is divided?

   (A) table of contents

   (B) **The dog ran in the yard.** sentence

---

5. What letters are not vowels?

   (A) **b, c, d, f, g, h, j, k, l, m, n, p, q, r, s, t, v, w, x, z** and sometimes **y** consonants

   (B)
   ```
   -all    -ack
   ball    back
   fall    tack
   -eat    -oat
   beat    boat
   seat    coat
   ```
   word families

---

6. Who writes stories?

   (A) illustrator

   (B) author

Name _____   Date _____   Helper _____

Language Arts – Sentence Completion

Directions: Read each sentence below. Complete each sentence using a vocabulary word from the Word/Picture Bank. Write the word in the blank.

Word/Picture Bank

author	directions	fantasy	language	period
table of contents	question	illustrator	chapter	poems

1. Who is the _____ of *Little House on the Prairie*?

2. Look in the _____ to find the page number for Chapter 3.

3. The _____ will tell you how to put the bike together.

4. Do you have a _____ about anything on the menu?

5. A story about a friendly mermaid is a _____.

6. Jack is the best _____ to draw pictures for the pirate story.

7. Seth's native _____ is English, but he speaks Spanish too.

8. I only have one more _____ to read in my book.

9. You must put a _____ at the end of each sentence.

10. I like reading _____ that rhyme.

_____   _____   _____
Name   Date   Helper

#BKCRD-44 Core Curriculum Vocab Cards Fun Sheets – Level 1 • ©2012 Super Duper® Publications • www.superduperinc.com

Language Arts – Sentence Completion

Directions: Read each sentence below. Complete each sentence using a vocabulary word from the Word/Picture Bank. Write the word in the blank.

Word/Picture Bank

middle	**a e i o u** and sometimes **y** vowels	Where do you live **?** question mark	predict	question
b, c, d, f, g, h, j, k, l, m, n, p, q, r, s, t, v, w, x, z and sometimes **y** **consonants**	order	**We won!** exclamation point	character	fiction

1. Rachel has four _____ in her name.

2. Jessie stood in the _____ of her two friends.

3. Letters that are not consonants are _____.

4. Put the students in _____ from tallest to shortest.

5. An _____ shows that a sentence has strong feeling.

6. The punctuation at the end of a question is a _____.

7. A _____ should have a question mark at the end.

8. No one can _____ how the story will end.

9. Made-up stories about people and events are _____.

10. Who is your favorite _____ in this story?

_____ _____ _____
Name   Date   Helper

Language Arts – Sentence Completion

Directions: Read each sentence below. Complete each sentence using a vocabulary word from the Word/Picture Bank. Write the word in the blank.

Word/Picture Bank

-all -ack ball back fall tack -eat -oat beat boat seat coat	**? , ! .**	The dog ran in the yard.		
word families	punctuation	sentence	character	fiction
	but – ter – fly	**apple** **Apple**		
vocabulary	syllables	capitalize	predict	question

1. There are two _____ in the word *baseball*.

2. You must always _____ the first letter of your name.

3. The main _____ in the story lived alone in the forest.

4. I like to read _____ more than true stories.

5. Can you _____ what will happen at the end of the story?

6. _____ end with the same letters and rhyme.

7. The sentences and questions must have correct _____.

8. We must answer the _____ at the end of the story.

9. Your _____ must be a complete thought.

10. Sara uses the dictionary to expand her _____.

_____ _____ _____
Name   Date   Helper

#BKCRD-44 Core Curriculum Vocab Cards Fun Sheets – Level 1 • ©2012 Super Duper® Publications • www.superduperinc.com

Language Arts – Which Ones Belong Together?

Directions: Cut out the three pictures in Row 1. Glue the two pictures that go together in the empty boxes on the left. Tell why the two pictures go together. Complete the page one row at a time.

1.

2.

3.

4.

5.

6.

1.

directions	illustrator	author

2.

-all -ack ball back fall tack -eat -oat beat boat seat coat	a e i o u and sometimes **y**	Roses are red, violets are blue. Sugar is sweet, and so are you!
word families	vowels	poems

3.

fiction	fantasy	middle

4.

chapter	fantasy	table of contents

5.

We won! exclamation point	The dog ran in the yard. sentence	question

6.

b, c, d, f, g, h, j, k, l, m, n, p, q, r, s, t, v, w, x, z and sometimes **y** consonants	a e i o u and sometimes **y** vowels	Ava is a smart girl. period

_____   _____   _____
Name   Date   Helper

Language Arts – Which Doesn't Belong?

Directions: Read/Listen carefully to each group of words. Mark an X through the word that doesn't belong. Tell how the other words relate to each other.

1. period, question mark, exclamation point, author

2. consonants, vowels, vocabulary, question mark

3. language, vocabulary, capitalize, word families

4. fiction, author, fantasy, middle

5. sentence, table of contents, period, vocabulary

6. author, illustrator, fiction, middle

7. exclamation point, consonant, vowels, word families

b, c, d, f, g, h, j, k, l, m, n, p, q, r, s, t, v, w, x, z and sometimes **y**

8. sentence, question, capitalize, language

9. order, table of contents, chapter, period

10. consonants, vowels, syllables, fantasy

_____ _____ _____
Name   Date   Helper

#BKCRD-44 Core Curriculum Vocab Cards Fun Sheets – Level 1 • ©2012 Super Duper® Publications • www.superduperinc.com

Language Arts – What Doesn't Belong?

Directions: Put an X through the picture in each row that doesn't belong. Tell why the other two pictures belong together.

1.

We won **!**

exclamation point

Roses are red,
violets are blue.
Sugar is sweet,
and so are you!

poems

Where do you live **?**

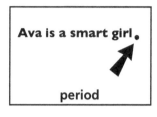

question mark

2.

b, c, d, f, g,
h, j, k, l, m,
n, p, q, r, s,
t, v, w, x, z
and sometimes y

consonants

a e i o u
and sometimes **y**

vowels

Ava is a smart girl **.**

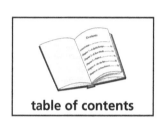

period

3.

directions

chapter

table of contents

4.

illustrator

author

predict

5.

order

English
Español
Português

language

middle

6.

vocabulary

fantasy

fiction

#BKCRD-44 *Core Curriculum Vocab Cards Fun Sheets – Level 1* • ©2012 Super Duper® Publications • www.superduperinc.com

Language Arts – Say It, Paste It - Initial

Directions: Have the student cut out the pictures at the bottom of the page. The Helper names a picture aloud, then the student glues/tapes or places it on the big picture with the same *beginning* sound.

Ava is a smart girl.	The dog ran in the yard.	? , ! .	Roses are red, violets are blue. Sugar is sweet, and so are you!	b, c, d, f, g, h, j, k, l, m, n, p, q, r, s, t, v, w, x, z and sometimes y
period	sentence	punctuation	poems	consonants
but – ter – fly			apple Apple	
syllables	fiction	fantasy	capitalize	character

#BKCRD-44 *Core Curriculum Vocab Cards Fun Sheets – Level 1* • ©2012 Super Duper® Publications • www.superduperinc.com

Language Arts – Say It, Paste It - Final

Directions: Have the student cut out the pictures at the bottom of the page. The Helper names a picture aloud, then the student glues/tapes or places it on the big picture with the same *ending* sound.

Name	Date	Helper

predict	question	character	sentence	fiction

The dog ran in the yard. — sentence

illustrator	consonants	exclamation point	chapter	punctuation

b, c, d, f, g, h, j, k, l, m, n, p, q, r, s, t, v, w, x, z and sometimes y — consonants

We won! — exclamation point

Language Arts – Breakdown

Directions: Have the student cut out the pictures. The student names each picture aloud and counts how many syllables (or parts of the word) it has. The student glues/tapes or places the picture on the side of the page with that number.

# 2 syllables	# 3 syllables

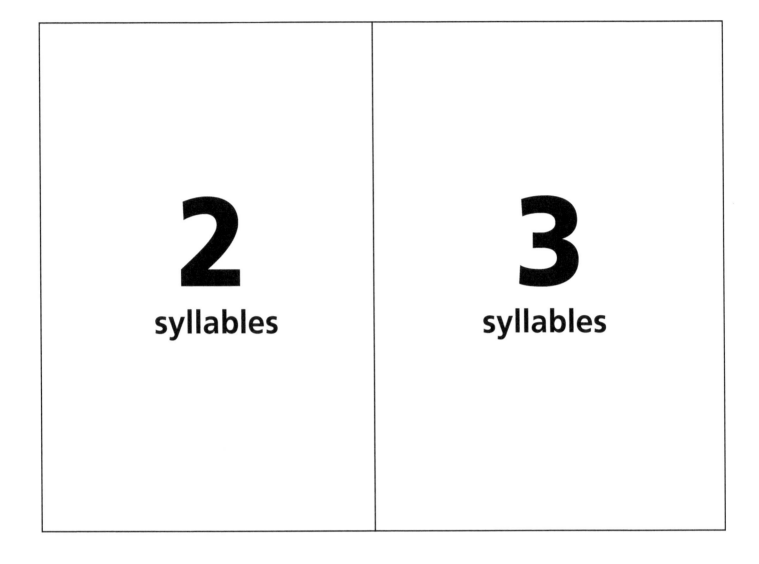

Name   Date   Helper

Where do you live **?**
question mark

character

Ava is a smart girl **.**
period

a e i o u
and sometimes **y**
vowels

fiction

English
Español
Português
language

middle

fantasy

The dog ran
in the yard.
sentence

but – ter – fly
syllables

Language Arts – Syllable Search

Directions: Have the student cut out the pictures. The student names each picture aloud and counts how many syllables (or parts of the word) it has. The student glues/tapes or places the picture on the side of the page with that number. Have the student find the three words that cannot be used and the tell number of syllables these words have.

4 **syllables**	**5** **syllables**

Name	Date	Helper

| 
vocabulary | -all -ack
ball back
fall tack
-eat -oat
beat boat
seat coat
word families | but – ter – fly
• • •
syllables | ? , ! .
punctuation | Where do you live ?
question mark |
| **a**pple
Apple
capitalize | directions | We won !
exclamation point | illustrator | table of contents |

Language Arts – Word Scramble Riddle

Directions: Unscramble the words to name each picture and write the letters in the blanks. Write the letters in circles in order in the blanks at the bottom of the page to answer the riddle.

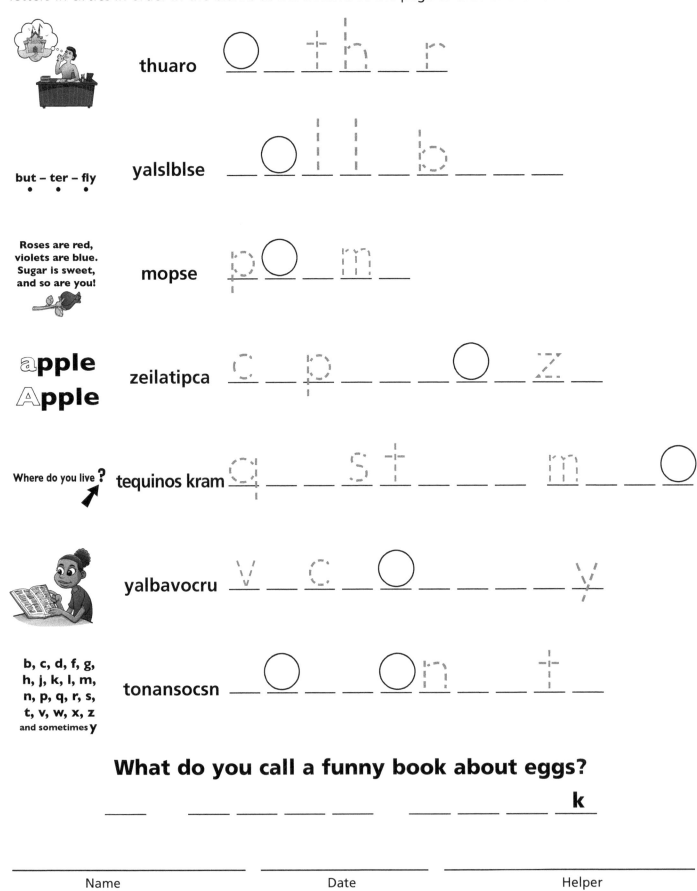

thuaro   (○) _ t h _ r

but – ter – fly   yalslblse   _ (○) l l _ b _ _ _

Roses are red, violets are blue. Sugar is sweet, and so are you!   mopse   p (○) _ m _

apple Apple   zeilatipca   c _ p _ _ _ (○) _ z _

Where do you live?   tequinos kram   q _ _ s t _ _ _ m _ _ (○)

yalbavocru   v _ c _ (○) _ _ _ y

b, c, d, f, g, h, j, k, l, m, n, p, q, r, s, t, v, w, x, z and sometimes y   tonansocsn   _ (○) _ _ (○) n _ t

What do you call a funny book about eggs?

_ _ _ _ _ _ _ _ _ k

_____   _____   _____
Name   Date   Helper

#BKCRD-44 Core Curriculum Vocab Cards Fun Sheets – Level 1 • ©2012 Super Duper® Publications • www.superduperinc.com

Language Arts – Word Scramble Riddle

Directions: Unscramble the words to name each picture and write the letters in the blanks. Write the letters in circles in order in the blanks at the bottom of the page to answer the riddle.

tafnsya   f __ __ t __ (O) __

tpricde   __ __ (e) __ i __ (O)

oiredp   __ (e) __ (O) __ (d)

Ava is a smart girl.

ncftioi   __ i __ t __ (O)

rtpache   (c) __ __ (p) __ (O)(O)

a e i o u
and sometimes **y**

lowesv   __ (o) __ (O)(O)(s)

delidm   __ __ (d) __ (O) __ (e)

What do you call a fairy that hasn't taken a bath?

____ ____ ____ **k** ____ ____ **b** ____ ____ ____ **!**

_____   _____   _____
Name   Date   Helper

Language Arts – Word Scramble Riddle

Directions: Unscramble the words to name each picture and write the letters in the blanks. Write the letters in circles in order in the blanks at the bottom of the page to answer the riddle.

but – ter – fly   **seylabsll**

drroe

horatu

iraltrsutol

Ava is a smart girl   **ropdei**

letba fo nntostec

English
Español
Português   **angelgua**

-all   -ack
ball   back
fall   tack
-eat   -oat
beat   boat
seat   coat   **wodr falsimei**

How do you talk to a giant?

____ ____ ____   ____ ____ i ____ ____   ____ ____ ____ ____ ____ ____!

_____   _____   _____
Name   Date   Helper

#BKCRD-44 Core Curriculum Vocab Cards Fun Sheets – Level 1 • ©2012 Super Duper® Publications • www.superduperinc.com

Language Arts – Definition Writing

Directions: Read the vocabulary word below each picture. Then, write a sentence beside each picture using the vocabulary word. Use the definition clues at the bottom of the page to help you.

1. **fiction**
    _____
    _____
    _____

2. **question**
    _____
    _____
    _____

3. **middle**
    _____
    _____
    _____

4. English
    Español
    Português
    language
    _____
    _____
    _____

5. **We won!**
    exclamation point
    _____
    _____
    _____

6. **a e i o u**
    and sometimes y
    vowels
    _____
    _____
    _____

a made-up story about people or events	something or someone in the center	a mark showing a sentence has strong feeling
letters that are not consonants	how people talk with each other	what you ask to get an answer

Name	Date	Helper

Language Arts – Definition Writing

Directions: Read the vocabulary word below each picture. Then, write a sentence beside each picture using the vocabulary word. Use the definition clues at the bottom of the page to help you.

1. apple
   Apple
   capitalize
   _____
   _____
   _____

2. Ava is a smart girl.
   period
   _____
   _____
   _____

3. **chapter**
   _____
   _____
   _____

4. **directions**
   _____
   _____
   _____

5. ? , ! .
   punctuation
   _____
   _____
   _____

6. Where do you live ?
   question mark
   _____
   _____
   _____

a mark at the end of a sentence	marks we use when we write	the mark used after a question
a group of pages in a book	steps telling you how to do something	making lowercase letters uppercase

_____   _____   _____
Name   Date   Helper

#BKCRD-44 *Core Curriculum Vocab Cards Fun Sheets – Level 1* • ©2012 Super Duper® Publications • www.superduperinc.com

Language Arts – Definition Writing

Directions: Read the vocabulary word below each picture. Then, write a sentence beside each picture using the vocabulary word. Use the definition clues at the bottom of the page to help you.

1.
   table of contents
   _____
   _____
   _____

2. -all   -ack
   ball   back
   fall   tack
   -eat   -oat
   beat   boat
   seat   coat
   word families
   _____
   _____
   _____

3.
   order
   _____
   _____
   _____

4.
   vocabulary
   _____
   _____
   _____

5. **but – ter – fly**
   •   •   •
   syllables
   _____
   _____
   _____

6.
   author
   _____
   _____
   _____

a list telling how a book is divided	the way you arrange things	smaller parts of a word
a person who writes stories	groups of words ending with the same letters and rhyme	words you know

_____   _____   _____
Name   Date   Helper

Language Arts – Definition Writing

Directions: Read the vocabulary word below each picture. Then, write a sentence beside each picture using the vocabulary word. Use the definition clues at the bottom of the page to help you.

1.

   fantasy

   _____
   _____
   _____

2. **b, c, d, f, g, h, j, k, l, m, n, p, q, r, s, t, v, w, x, z** and sometimes **y**

   consonants

   _____
   _____
   _____

3.

   illustrator

   _____
   _____
   _____

4.

   predict

   _____
   _____
   _____

5.

   character

   _____
   _____
   _____

6. **Roses are red, violets are blue. Sugar is sweet, and so are you!**

   poems

   _____
   _____
   _____

a person or animal in a story	when you guess what will happen	short phrases or sentences that rhyme
letters that are NOT vowels	a person who draws pictures for a book	a magical make-believe story

Name _____   Date _____   Helper _____

#BKCRD-44 Core Curriculum Vocab Cards Fun Sheets – Level 1 • ©2012 Super Duper® Publications • www.superduperinc.com

Math – Definitions Match-Up

Directions: Draw a line from the definition in Column A to the word that matches it in Column B. Read/Say the definition and its matching vocabulary word aloud.

A   B

$$\begin{array}{r} 2 \\ +2 \\ \hline 4 \end{array}$$

This is putting two numbers together to make a bigger number.

minus

$$\begin{array}{r} 2 \\ -1 \\ \hline 1 \end{array}$$

This is the sign you use when you subtract numbers.

solve

8-6=2

This is taking one number away from another number.

addition

$$\begin{array}{r} 4 \\ +2 \\ \hline 6 \end{array}$$

This is the answer you get when you add two numbers together.

plus

This is what you do to find the answer to a math problem.

sum

$$\begin{array}{r} 2 \\ +1 \\ \hline 3 \end{array}$$

This is the sign you use when you add numbers together.

subtraction

_____   _____   _____
Name   Date   Helper

Math – Star Match-Up

Directions: Cut out the definitions at the bottom of the page. Shuffle the definitions and place them facedown. Have students take turns reading the definitions and placing them next to the correct pictures. The first player to find the star is the winner.

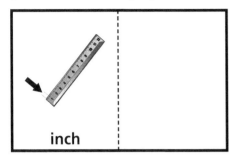
inch

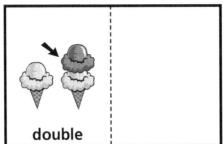
double

forward

pound

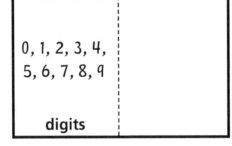
0, 1, 2, 3, 4, 5, 6, 7, 8, 9

digits

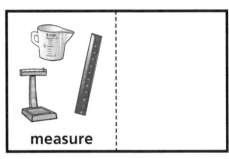
measure

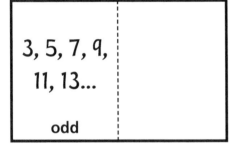
3, 5, 7, 9, 11, 13...

odd

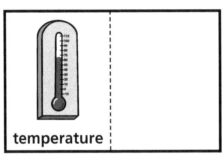
temperature

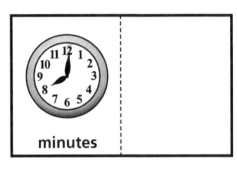
minutes

This is how you find the size or weight of something.	These are the numbers 0 to 9.	This is a measurement of weight that is the same as 16 ounces.	Twelve of these are equal to a foot.	There are 60 of these in an hour.
	This measurement tells how hot or cold something is.	This is when you make something two times as big.	This is the direction you go when you move to the front.	This is a number that has something left over when you divide it by 2.

_____   _____   _____
Name   Date   Helper

#BKCRD-44 *Core Curriculum Vocab Cards Fun Sheets – Level 1* • ©2012 Super Duper® Publications • www.superduperinc.com

Math – Treasure Chest Match-Up

Directions: Cut out the definitions at the bottom of the page. Shuffle the definitions and place them facedown. Have students take turns reading the definitions and placing them next to the correct pictures. The first player to find the treasure chest is the winner.

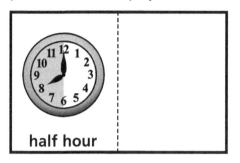
half hour

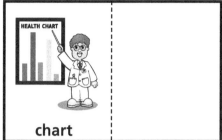
chart

backward

guess

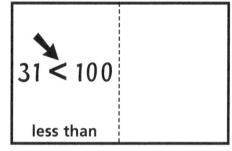
less than

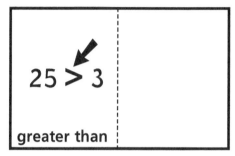
greater than

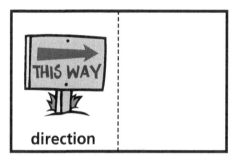
direction

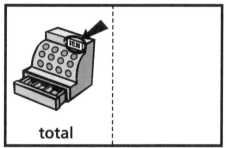
total

coin

This is the direction you go when you move to the rear.	This is a piece of metal used to buy things.	This is an answer that you are not sure is correct.	This can be a table, graph, or diagram that gives information.	This sign means that a number is smaller than another number.
	This sign means that a number is more than another number.	This is when you add everything together.	This is a unit of time that is the same as 30 minutes.	This is a way you go when walking or riding.

_____ _____ _____
Name   Date   Helper

#BKCRD-44 *Core Curriculum Vocab Cards Fun Sheets – Level 1* • ©2012 Super Duper® Publications • www.superduperinc.com

29

Math – What's the Correct Meaning?

Directions: Read each sentence. Circle the picture and definition on the right that have the correct meaning for the word in bold.

1. The digits in my phone number are all **even** numbers.

3, 5, 7, 9, 11, 13...

This is a number that has something left over when you divide it by 2.

2, 4, 6, 8, 10, 12...

This is a number that has nothing left over when you divide it by 2.

---

2. My shoelaces need to be one **inch** longer.

Twelve of these are equal to a foot.

There are 60 of these in an hour.

---

3. I bought a **pound** of apples to make a pie.

$$\begin{array}{r} 4 \\ +2 \\ \hline 6 \end{array}$$
This is the answer you get when you add two numbers together.

This is a measurement of weight that is the same as 16 ounces.

---

4. The houses with **odd** numbers are on the left side of the street.

3, 5, 7, 9, 11, 13...

This is a number that has something left over when you divide it by 2.

This is when you add everything together.

---

5. Dad ordered a **double** scoop of ice cream.

This is how you find the size or weight of something.

This is when you make something two times as big.

---

6. What is the **temperature** outside today?

THIS WAY
This is a way you go when walking or riding.

This measurement tells how hot or cold something is.

Name _____   Date _____   Helper _____

Math – What's the Correct Meaning?

Directions: Read each sentence. Circle the picture and definition on the right that have the correct meaning for the word in bold.

1. Jim moved **forward** to be the first in line.

This is the direction you go when you move to the rear.

This is the direction you go when you move to the front.

2. Mom records my height on a **chart**.

This is a piece of metal used to buy things.

This can be a table, graph, or diagram that gives information.

3. Can you **guess** how many cookies Mom baked?

This is an answer that you are not sure is correct.

This is the sign you use when you add numbers together.

4. The teacher helped me **solve** the math problem.

This is how you find the size or weight of something.

This is what you do to find the answer to a math problem.

5. Dan can hold his breath for two **minutes**.

This is when you add everything together.

There are 60 of these in an hour.

6. It takes a **half hour** to drive to Grandma's house.

This is a unit of time that is the same as 30 minutes.

This is putting two numbers together to make a bigger number.

Name   Date   Helper

Math – What's the Correct Meaning?

Directions: Read each sentence. Circle the picture and definition on the right that have the correct meaning for the word in bold.

1. You must **measure** the sugar first.

This is how you find the size or weight of something.

Twelve of these are equal to a foot.

2. Which **direction** should we go to find the library?

This is the direction you go when you move to the front.

This is a way you go when walking or riding.

3. The baby eats **less than** I do.

This sign means that a number is smaller than another number.

This is a measurement of weight that is the same as 16 ounces.

4. What is the **total** of our bill?

This is when you add everything together.

This is the sign you use when you subtract numbers.

5. I need another **coin** for the snack machine.

Twelve of these are equal to a foot.

This is a piece of metal used to buy things.

6. The amount of rain this year is **greater than** last year.

This sign means that a number is more than another number.

This is the sign you use when you add numbers together.

_____   _____   _____
Name   Date   Helper

#BKCRD-44 Core Curriculum Vocab Cards Fun Sheets – Level 1 • ©2012 Super Duper® Publications • www.superduperinc.com

Math – Answer It!

Directions: Read each question. Then, put an X on the letter next to the picture and vocabulary word that best answers the question.

1. What tells me the way to go?

   (A) measure   **(B)** direction

2. What do you do when you don't know the answer?

   (A) guess   **(B)**  solve

3. Which way takes me to the front of the line?

   (A) forward   **(B)** backward

4. What do I ask for to get twice as much ice cream?

   (A) double   **(B)** total

5. What tells me how hot or cold it is?

   (A) half hour   **(B)** temperature

6. What does Mom need to know before she pays for the groceries?

   (A) plus   **(B)** total

_____   _____   _____
Name   Date   Helper

Math – Answer It!

Directions: Read each question. Then, put an X on the letter next to the picture and vocabulary word that best answers the question.

1. What can I put in the snack machine to buy snacks?

    (A)
    coin

    (B)
    pound

2. What do I do to find out how much the dog weighs?

    (A)
    measure

    (B)
    chart

3. What kind of numbers are not even?

    (A) 25 > 3
    greater than

    (B) 3, 5, 7, 9, 11, 13...
    odd

4. Which sign tells me to add numbers?

    (A) $\begin{array}{r} 2 \\ +1 \\ \hline 3 \end{array}$
    plus

    (B) $\begin{array}{r} 2 \\ -1 \\ \hline 1 \end{array}$
    minus

5. Which do I use to find the sum of many numbers?

    (A)
    subtraction

    (B) $\begin{array}{r} 2 \\ +2 \\ \hline 4 \end{array}$
    addition

6. Which sign tells me to subtract numbers?

    (A) $\begin{array}{r} 2 \\ -1 \\ \hline 1 \end{array}$
    minus

    (B) 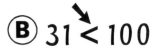 31 < 100
    less than

Name	Date	Helper

#BKCRD-44 *Core Curriculum Vocab Cards Fun Sheets – Level 1* • ©2012 Super Duper® Publications • www.superduperinc.com

Math – Answer It!

Directions: Read each question. Then, put an X on the letter next to the picture and vocabulary word that best answers the question.

1. Which is heavier?

   A
   pound

   B
   coin

2. What makes up a number?

   A 0, 1, 2, 3, 4, 5, 6, 7, 8, 9
   digits

   B
   chart

3. Which is less time?

   A
   minutes

   B
   half hour

4. Which tells us that one number is more than another?

   A 25 > 3
   greater than

   B
   backward

5. What is the answer to an addition problem?

   A
   $$\begin{array}{r} 2 \\ +1 \\ \hline 3 \end{array}$$
   plus

   B
   $$\begin{array}{r} 4 \\ +2 \\ \hline 6 \end{array}$$
   sum

6. Which would measure the width of a button?

   A
   total

   B
   inch

_____ _____ _____
Name   Date   Helper

Math – Sentence Completion

Directions: Read each sentence below. Complete each sentence using a vocabulary word from the Word/Picture Bank. Write the word in the blank.

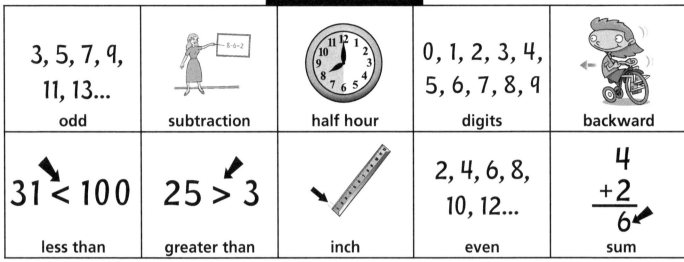

Word/Picture Bank

3, 5, 7, 9, 11, 13...	8-6=2	(clock)	0, 1, 2, 3, 4, 5, 6, 7, 8, 9	(bicycle)
odd	subtraction	half hour	digits	backward
31 < 100	25 > 3	(ruler)	2, 4, 6, 8, 10, 12...	4 +2 6
less than	greater than	inch	even	sum

1. We mowed the grass in a _____.

2. Mary uses the _____ numbers 6/12/82 to write her birth date.

3. Mom needed another _____ of ribbon to tie the bow.

4. It's hard to walk _____ because you can't see where you're going.

5. Dan is much better at addition than _____.

6. The _____ numbers 975-1331 make up my telephone number.

7. The _____ of our ages — 8, 12, 9, 5 — is 34.

8. The number 56 is _____ 46.

9. Twelve inches of snow is _____ the 18 inches we had last year.

10. How many _____ are in the number 1,357?

_____ _____ _____
Name   Date   Helper

#BKCRD-44 Core Curriculum Vocab Cards Fun Sheets – Level 1 • ©2012 Super Duper® Publications • www.superduperinc.com

Math – Sentence Completion

Directions: Read each sentence below. Complete each sentence using a vocabulary word from the Word/Picture Bank. Write the word in the blank.

Word/Picture Bank				
temperature	pound	double	guess	measure
total	minutes	forward	direction	coin

1. Can you help me _____ the sugar and flour for the cookies?

2. The _____ today may reach 90°.

3. The _____ of our bill was $23.17.

4. There is more than a _____ of butter in the cake.

5. How many _____ before recess?

6. Mary's big bowl of ice cream was _____ the size of mine.

7. Jeff moved _____ to get near the stage.

8. You'll never _____ how many candies Rob ate.

9. Maria sent us in the wrong _____, and we got lost.

10. President Lincoln's face is on the one-cent _____.

_____ _____ _____
Name   Date   Helper

Math – Sentence Completion

Directions: Read each sentence below. Complete each sentence using a vocabulary word from the Word/Picture Bank. Write the word in the blank.

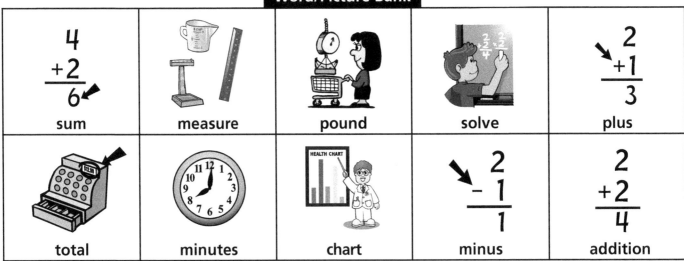

		Word/Picture Bank		
sum	measure	pound	solve	plus
total	minutes	chart	minus	addition

1. The hamburgers cost us a _____ of $8.59.

2. We forgot to _____ the weight of each puppy.

3. It takes 16 ounces to make one _____.

4. Will must use _____ to find the sum of 27 and 79.

5. A _____ sign tells you to add the numbers together.

6. The teacher graphs our team scores on a _____ so we can see who is winning!

7. How many _____ make one hour?

8. Dad must use a calculator to _____ the problem.

9. The _____ sign tells us to subtract the numbers to get an answer.

10. Adding numbers together results in a _____.

_____   _____   _____
       Name   Date   Helper

#BKCRD-44 Core Curriculum Vocab Cards Fun Sheets – Level 1 • ©2012 Super Duper® Publications • www.superduperinc.com

Math – Which Ones Belong Together?

Directions: Cut out the three pictures in Row 1. Glue the two pictures that go together in the empty boxes on the left. Tell why the two pictures go together. Complete the page one row at a time.

1.		
2.		
3.		
4.		
5.		
6.		

1.

$$\begin{array}{r} 2 \\ -\ 1 \\ \hline 1 \end{array}$$

minus

$$\begin{array}{r} 4 \\ +\ 2 \\ \hline 6 \end{array}$$

sum

8-6=2

subtraction

2.

2, 4, 6, 8, 10, 12...

even

3, 5, 7, 9, 11, 13...

odd

coin

3.

half hour

inch

minutes

4.

backward

forward

temperature

5.

chart

direction

backward

6.

total

31 < 100

less than

25 > 3

greater than

_____ _____ _____
Name   Date   Helper

Math – Which Doesn't Belong?

Directions: Read/Listen carefully to each group of words. Mark an X through the word that doesn't belong. Tell how the other words relate to each other.

$$\begin{array}{r} 2 \\ +2 \\ \hline 4 \end{array}$$

1. backward, temperature, direction, forward

2. addition, inch, plus, total

3. minutes, total, addition, subtraction

$31 < 100$

4. inch, pound, digits, temperature

5. digits, odd, inch, even

6. half hour, guess, minutes, temperature

7. total, double, chart, sum

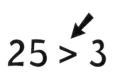

$25 > 3$

8. forward, temperature, backward, direction

9. solve, total, coin, sum

10. addition, inch, minutes, temperature

_____ _____ _____
Name   Date   Helper

#BKCRD-44 *Core Curriculum Vocab Cards Fun Sheets – Level 1* • ©2012 Super Duper® Publications • www.superduperinc.com

Math – What Doesn't Belong?

Directions: Put an X through the picture in each row that doesn't belong. Tell why the other two pictures belong together.

1.
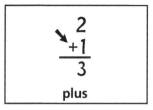

plus

3, 5, 7, 9,
11, 13...

odd

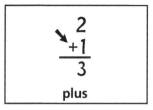

minus

2.
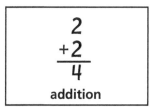

addition

subtraction

2, 4, 6, 8,
10, 12...

even

3.
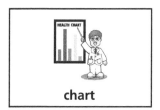

chart

forward

backward

4.

half hour

0, 1, 2, 3, 4,
5, 6, 7, 8, 9

digits

minutes

5.
31 < 100

less than

3, 5, 7, 9,
11, 13...

odd

2, 4, 6, 8,
10, 12...

even

6.
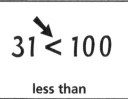

4
+2
6

sum

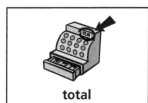

total

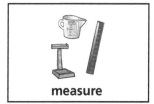

measure

_____   _____   _____
Name   Date   Helper

Math – Say It, Paste It - Initial

Directions: Have the student cut out the pictures at the bottom of the page. The Helper names a picture aloud, then the student glues/tapes or places it on the big picture with the same *beginning* sound.

#BKCRD-44 *Core Curriculum Vocab Cards Fun Sheets – Level 1* • ©2012 Super Duper® Publications • www.superduperinc.com

Math – Say It, Paste It - Final

Directions: Have the student cut out the pictures at the bottom of the page. The Helper names a picture aloud, then the student glues/tapes or places it on the big picture with the same *ending* sound.

Name	Date		Helper	
3, 5, 7, 9, 11, 13... **odd**	THIS WAY **direction**	**forward**	**total**	2, 4, 6, 8, 10, 12... **even**
double	2 +1 / 3 **plus**	**guess**	2 − 1 / 1 **minus**	**pound**

Math – Breakdown

Directions: Have the student cut out the pictures. The student names each picture aloud and counts how many syllables (or parts of the word) it has. The student glues/tapes or places the picture on the side of the page with that number.

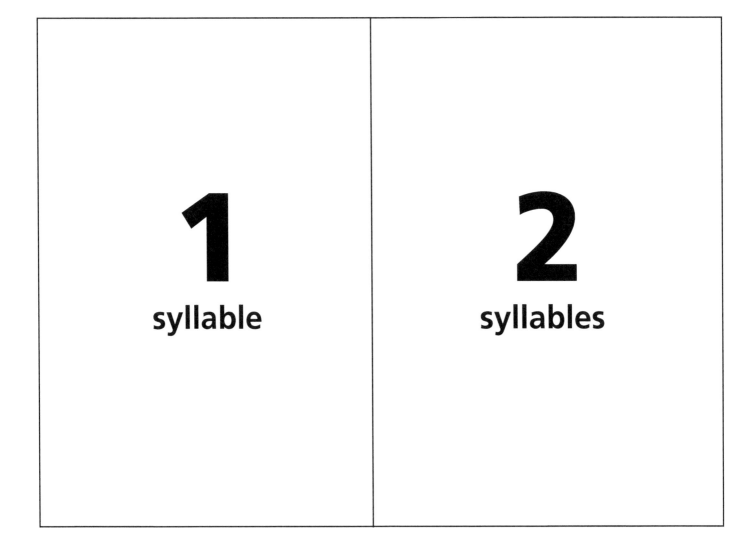

1 syllable	**2** syllables

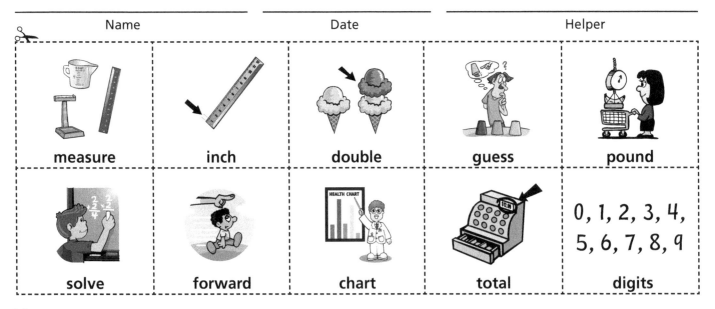

measure	inch	double	guess	pound
solve	forward	chart	total	0, 1, 2, 3, 4, 5, 6, 7, 8, 9 digits

Math – Syllable Search

Directions: Have the student cut out the pictures. The student names each picture aloud and counts how many syllables (or parts of the word) it has. The student glues/tapes or places the picture on the side of the page with that number.

2 syllables	**3** syllables

Name   Date   Helper

25 > 3	$\frac{\begin{array}{r} 2 \\ -1 \end{array}}{1}$	THIS WAY	(clock)	(child on tricycle)
greater than	**minus**	**direction**	**minutes**	**backward**
2, 4, 6, 8, 10, 12...	$\frac{\begin{array}{r} 2 \\ +2 \end{array}}{4}$	(clock)	31 < 100	(teacher at board 8-6=2)
even	**addition**	**half hour**	**less than**	**subtraction**

Math – Word Scramble Riddle

Directions: Unscramble the words to name each picture and write the letters in the blanks. Write the letters in circles in order in the blanks at the bottom of the page to answer the riddle.

31 < 100   sles nhta    ◯ __ __ s t __ __ __

   ncio   __ ◯ __ ◯

   suegs   ◯ __ e __ s

2
+2
4   nadoditi   __ __ __ __ __ ◯◯ __ n

esumrae   ◯◯ __ __ s __ r __

vosel   ◯ __ l __ ◯

What did the beach say when the tide came in?

__ __ __ __   __ __ __ __ __   **no** __ __ **a !**

_____ _____ _____
Name   Date   Helper

46   #BKCRD-44 Core Curriculum Vocab Cards Fun Sheets – Level 1 • ©2012 Super Duper® Publications • www.superduperinc.com

Math – Word Scramble Riddle

Directions: Unscramble the words to name each picture and write the letters in the blanks. Write the letters in circles in order in the blanks at the bottom of the page to answer the riddle.

   cwkbraad

   tchra

   ertematupre

$$\begin{array}{r} 2 \\ +1 \\ \hline 3 \end{array}$$ slup

$25 > 3$ rgteare naht

   ledubo

How do rabbits travel?

On __ __ __ __ __ __ __ __ __ __ __!

_____   _____   _____
Name   Date   Helper

Math – Word Scramble Riddle

Directions: Unscramble the words to name each picture and write the letters in the blanks. Write the letters in circles in order in the blanks at the bottom of the page to answer the riddle.

 dunpo — ⬤ u ⬤ d

 sles nhta — ___ ___ ___ ___ ⬤ ⬤ ___ n

 emreuas — ⬤ ___ s ___ r ___

 nridoeict — ⬤ ⬤ ___ ___ t ___ ___ ___

 awdfrro — ⬤ ___ r ___ a ___ ___

 vnee — ⬤ v ⬤ ___

 thcra — ___ h ___ ___ ⬤

Where did the Pilgrims land when they arrived in America?

___ ___ ___ ___ ___ ___ ___ ___ ___ ___ ___ ___!

#BKCRD-44 Core Curriculum Vocab Cards Fun Sheets – Level 1 • ©2012 Super Duper® Publications • www.superduperinc.com

Name   Date   Helper

Math – Definition Writing

Directions: Read the vocabulary word below each picture. Then, write a sentence beside each picture using the vocabulary word. Use the definition clues at the bottom of the page to help you.

1.

   direction

   _____
   _____
   _____

2. $31 < 100$

   less than

   _____
   _____
   _____

3.

   guess

   _____
   _____
   _____

4. $\begin{array}{r} 2 \\ +2 \\ \hline 4 \end{array}$

   addition

   _____
   _____
   _____

5.

   solve

   _____
   _____
   _____

6.

   measure

   _____
   _____
   _____

give an answer that you aren't sure is correct	a sign meaning that one number is smaller than another	putting two numbers together to make a bigger number
to find the size or weight of something	the way you go	to find the answer to a problem

_____   _____   _____
Name   Date   Helper

Math – Definition Writing

Directions: Read the vocabulary word below each picture. Then, write a sentence beside each picture using the vocabulary word. Use the definition clues at the bottom of the page to help you.

1.
$$\begin{array}{r} 4 \\ +2 \\ \hline 6 \end{array}$$
sum
_____
_____
_____

2.
double
_____
_____
_____

3.
subtraction
_____
_____
_____

4.
forward
_____
_____
_____

5.
0, 1, 2, 3, 4,
5, 6, 7, 8, 9
digits
_____
_____
_____

6.
coin
_____
_____
_____

make something twice as big	taking one number away from another	the numbers 0 to 9
a piece of metal used to buy things	moving to the front	the answer when you add two numbers

_____   _____   _____
Name   Date   Helper

#BKCRD-44 Core Curriculum Vocab Cards Fun Sheets – Level 1 • ©2012 Super Duper® Publications • www.superduperinc.com

Math – Definition Writing

Directions: Read the vocabulary word below each picture. Then, write a sentence beside each picture using the vocabulary word. Use the definition clues at the bottom of the page to help you.

1. **chart** _____

2. 2, 4, 6, 8, 10, 12... **even** _____

3. **pound** _____

4. **temperature** _____

5. **inch** _____

6. 2 - 1 / 1 **minus** _____

twelve of these are equal to a foot	the same as 16 ounces	a table, graph, or diagram of information
the measurement telling how hot or cold something is	the sign you use to subtract numbers	numbers with no remainder when divided by two

Name	Date	Helper

Math – Definition Writing

Directions: Read the vocabulary word below each picture. Then, write a sentence beside each picture using the vocabulary word. Use the definition clues at the bottom of the page to help you.

1. **minutes** _____

2. **half hour** _____

3. **total** _____

4. 3, 5, 7, 9, 11, 13... **odd** _____

5. 25 > 3 **greater than** _____

6. **backward** _____

numbers when divided by two have a remainder	to move to the rear or move in reverse	a sign meaning one number is more than another
when you add everything together	60 of these make up an hour	a time of 30 minutes

_____   _____   _____
Name   Date   Helper

#BKCRD-44 *Core Curriculum Vocab Cards Fun Sheets – Level 1* • ©2012 Super Duper® Publications • www.superduperinc.com

Science – Definitions Match-Up

Directions: Draw a line from the definition in Column A to the word that matches it in Column B. Read/Say the definition and its matching vocabulary word aloud.

A

This is a very large body of salt water.

This is a state of matter, like juice, water, or milk.

This is something on the beach that you use to make castles.

These are the different times of the year called winter, spring, summer, and fall.

This is the air above the Earth where there are clouds and birds.

This is what you do to make something warmer.

B

heat

sky

seasons

ocean

liquid

sand

Name   Date   Helper

Science – Star Match-Up

Directions: Cut out the definitions at the bottom of the page. Shuffle the definitions and place them facedown. Have students take turns reading the definitions and placing them next to the correct picture. The first player to find the star is the winner.

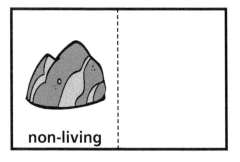
non-living

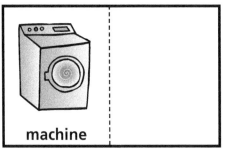
machine

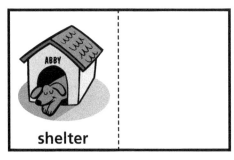
shelter

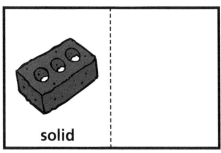
solid

mixture

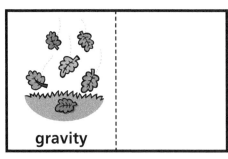
gravity

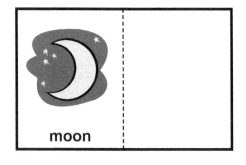
moon

sunlight

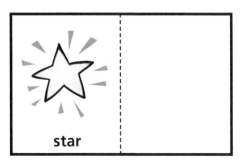
star

This is a bright light that twinkles in the night sky.	This is anything that has moving parts and does a job.	This is a state of matter that is hard.	This is a large object that circles the earth and lights the sky at night.	This is the pull of the Earth that makes objects fall to the ground.
	This is the light that comes from the sun.	This is something that protects people or animals from bad weather.	This is what you get when you put two or more things together to make one thing.	This is anything that does not breathe or eat.

_____ _____ _____
Name   Date   Helper

#BKCRD-44 *Core Curriculum Vocab Cards Fun Sheets – Level 1* • ©2012 Super Duper® Publications • www.superduperinc.com

Science – Treasure Chest Match-Up

Directions: Cut out the definitions at the bottom of the page. Shuffle the definitions and place them facedown. Have students take turns reading the definitions and placing them next to the correct pictures. The first player to find the treasure chest is the winner.

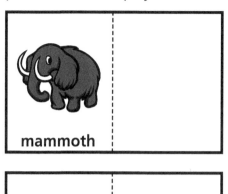

mammoth

salt water

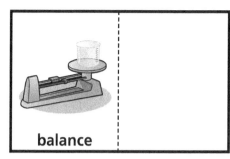

balance

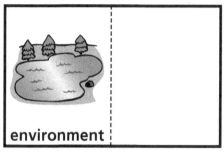

environment

dinosaur

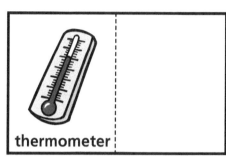

thermometer

location

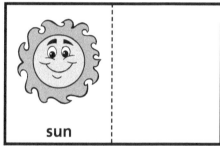

sun

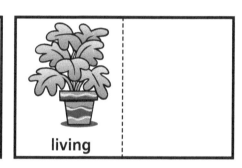

living

This animal looked like a large lizard and lived a long time ago.	This is the land, plants, animals, water, and trees that surround us.	This is a specific place.	This is a tool used to measure weight.	This is a tool that tells how hot or cold something is.
(treasure chest image)	This is a giant object in the sky that heats and lights the Earth.	This animal looked like an elephant and lived a long time ago.	This is what you get when you mix water and salt together.	This is the act of breathing and eating.

_____   _____   _____
Name   Date   Helper

Science – What's the Correct Meaning?

Directions: Read each sentence. Circle the picture and definition on the right that have the correct meaning for the word in bold.

1. You must **freeze** the water.

This is a state of matter, like juice, water, or milk.

This is what you do to a liquid to make it hard.

2. Rocks, rain, and sand are **non-living**.

This is anything that does not breathe or eat.

This is the act of breathing and eating.

3. Everyone needs food and **shelter**.

This is a large object that circles the earth and lights the sky at night.

This is something that protects people or animals from bad weather.

4. The buckets were heavy when we filled them with **sand**.

This is something on the beach that you use to make castles.

This is what you get when you put two or more things together to make one thing.

5. A **machine** fills all the bottles with juice.

This is a tool used to measure weight.

This is anything that has moving parts and does a job.

6. Everyone should help keep our **environment** clean.

This is a specific place.

This is the land, plants, animals, water, and trees that surround us.

_____   _____   _____
Name   Date   Helper

Science – What's the Correct Meaning?

Directions: Read each sentence. Circle the picture and definition on the right that has the correct meaning for the word in bold.

1. Trees, people, and animals are **living** things.

This is the act of breathing and eating.

This is anything that does not breathe or eat.

2. The **thermometer** says it's 85° outside.

This is a tool that tells how hot or cold something is.

This is a tool used to measure weight.

3. Can you find our **location** on the map?

These are the different times of the year called winter, spring, summer, and fall.

This is a specific place.

4. It is dangerous to look directly at the **sun**.

This is a large object that circles the earth and lights the sky at night.

This is a giant object in the sky that heats and lights the Earth.

5. The campfire will **heat** the area around our campsite.

This is what you do to make something warmer.

This is a bright light that twinkles in the night sky.

6. The **sky** is bright blue today.

This is a very large body of salt water.

This is the air above the Earth where there are clouds and birds.

_____   _____   _____
Name   Date   Helper

Science – What's the Correct Meaning?

Directions: Read each sentence. Circle the picture and definition on the right that have the correct meaning for the word in bold.

1. Which of the **seasons** is your favorite?

This is the land, plants, animals, water, and trees that surround us.

These are the different times of the year called winter, spring, summer, and fall.

2. Soda is a **liquid**.

This is what you get when you mix water and salt together.

This is a state of matter, like juice, water, or milk.

3. I love to swim in the **ocean**.

This is a very large body of salt water.

This is what you get when you put two or more things together to make one thing.

4. The walls of the house are strong and **solid**.

This is a state of matter that is hard.

This is the pull of the Earth that makes objects fall to the ground.

5. A **mixture** of juice and water is delicious.

This is what you get when you put two or more things together to make one thing.

This is what you do to a liquid to make it hard.

6. If not for **gravity**, we would float into space.

This is the pull of the Earth that makes objects fall to the ground.

This is the air above the Earth where there are clouds and birds.

Name   Date   Helper

#BKCRD-44 Core Curriculum Vocab Cards Fun Sheets – Level 1 • ©2012 Super Duper® Publications • www.superduperinc.com

Science – Answer It!

Directions: Read each question. Then put an X on the letter next to the picture and vocabulary word that best answers the question.

1. What are the four changes in our weather called?

   environment

   seasons

---

2. What do we drink?

   liquid

   solid

---

3. What do whales, fish, and octopi live in?

   mixture

   ocean

---

4. What kinds of materials do we use to build houses?

   solid

   living

---

5. What makes things stay on the ground?

   moon

   gravity

---

6. What are the warm bright rays coming from the sky?

   sunlight

   star

Name	Date	Helper

Science – Answer It!

Directions: Read each question. Then, put an X on the letter next to the picture and vocabulary word that best answers the question.

1. What twinkles in the night sky?

   A
   star

   B
   sun

---

2. Which animal looks like an elephant?

   A
   dinosaur

   B
   mammoth

---

3. What kind of water do oceans and seas usually have?

   A
   salt water

   B
   freeze

---

4. What tells us one thing is heavier than another?

   A
   thermometer

   B
   balance

---

5. What prehistoric animal once roamed Earth?

   A
   dinosaur

   B
   shelter

---

6. What do you have after stirring fruit juice and water?

   A
   mixture

   B
   solid

| Name | Date | Helper |

#BKCRD-44 *Core Curriculum Vocab Cards Fun Sheets – Level 1* • ©2012 Super Duper® Publications • www.superduperinc.com

Science – Answer It!

Directions: Read each question. Then, put an X on the letter next to the picture and vocabulary word that best answers the question.

1. What do you do to water to make ice? (A) mixture (B) freeze

2. What are things that don't eat or breathe? (A) living (B) non-living

3. Which do we need to survive? (A) dinosaur (B) shelter

4. What do you play in on the beach? (A) sand (B) solid

5. What helps us do work? (A) mammoth (B) machine

6. What makes up all the things around us? (A) environment (B) location

_____   _____   _____
Name   Date   Helper

Science – Sentence Completion

Directions: Read each sentence below. Complete each sentence using a vocabulary word from the Word/Picture Bank. Write the word in the blank.

Word/Picture Bank

seasons	ocean	gravity	star	salt water
liquid	solid	sunlight	mammoth	balance

1. Let's use the _____ to compare the weight of the apple and strawberry.

2. The force of _____ keeps us on the ground.

3. Would you like to swim in the _____?

4. Fall and summer are my favorite _____.

5. Juice is a _____.

6. The rays of warm _____ came through the window.

7. We need _____ materials to build the tree house.

8. Have you ever wished upon a _____?

9. The _____ had long tusks like the elephants at the zoo.

10. Oceans are made up of _____.

_____ _____ _____
Name   Date   Helper

#BKCRD-44 Core Curriculum Vocab Cards Fun Sheets – Level 1 • ©2012 Super Duper® Publications • www.superduperinc.com

Science – Sentence Completion

Directions: Read each sentence below. Complete each sentence using a vocabulary word from the Word/Picture Bank. Write the word in the blank.

Word/Picture Bank

dinosaur	mixture	environment	machine	sand
freeze	non-living	shelter	living	thermometer

1. The _____ shows that it's 36° outside.

2. Which _____ do you think was the scariest?

3. What would a _____ of grape juice and lemonade taste like?

4. Dad built a _____ to help him rake leaves.

5. When it starts raining, I find _____ to keep me dry.

6. Mother likes to _____ the leftover soup and heat it again later.

7. Everyone should help keep our _____ free of trash.

8. People and other _____ things need food, water, and air to survive.

9. Jewelry, dishes, and cell phones are _____ things.

10. I love playing in the _____ when I go to the beach.

_____   _____   _____
Name   Date   Helper

Science – Sentence Completion

Directions: Read each sentence below. Complete each sentence using a vocabulary word from the Word/Picture Bank. Write the word in the blank.

Word/Picture Bank

| location | heat | moon | gravity | dinosaur |
| sun | sky | balance | thermometer | mixture |

1. I cannot find my _____ on this map.

2. The airplane flew high in the _____.

3. A _____ can tell you which of two items is heavier.

4. We use our fireplace to _____ the family room.

5. The _____ lit our path through the dark woods at night.

6. Making a _____ of different fruit juices would be yummy.

7. When I'm sick, Mom uses a small _____ to check my temperature.

8. It's hard to walk on the moon because there is very little _____.

9. The heat from the _____ warms Earth from millions of miles away.

10. Scientists use fossils to rebuild the body of a _____ to see what it looked like.

_____   _____   _____
Name   Date   Helper

#BKCRD-44 Core Curriculum Vocab Cards Fun Sheets – Level 1 • ©2012 Super Duper® Publications • www.superduperinc.com

Science – Which Ones Belong Together?

Directions: Cut out the three pictures in Row 1. Glue the two pictures that go together in the empty boxes on the left. Tell why the two pictures go together. Complete the page one row at a time.

1.

1. living   non-living   location

2.

2. solid   seasons   liquid

3.

3. sky   salt water   ocean

4.

4. moon   sand   sun

5.

5. mammoth   shelter   dinosaur

6.

6. star   thermometer   balance

_____   _____   _____
Name   Date   Helper

Science – Which Doesn't Belong?

Directions: Read/Listen carefully to each group of words. Mark an X through the word that doesn't belong. Tell how the other words relate to each other.

1. sun, moon, star, gravity

2. solid, liquid, ocean, salt water

3. heat, sunlight, freeze, sun

4. mammoth, non-living, dinosaur, living

5. machine, thermometer, freeze, balance

6. seasons, mixture, environment, thermometer

7. liquid, salt water, shelter, ocean

8. sky, liquid, moon, sun

9. ocean, sand, salt water, star

10. non-living, sand, living, moon

_____ _____ _____
Name   Date   Helper

#BKCRD-44 *Core Curriculum Vocab Cards Fun Sheets – Level 1* • ©2012 Super Duper® Publications • www.superduperinc.com

Science – What Doesn't Belong?

Directions: Put an X through the picture in each row that doesn't belong. Tell why the other two pictures belong together.

1.
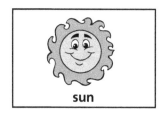 sun   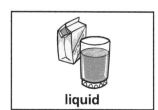 liquid   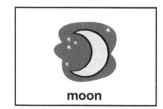 moon

2.
 mixture    salt water   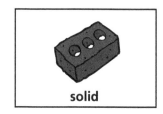 solid

3.
 heat    star    freeze

4.
 balance    sunlight   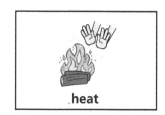 heat

5.
 mammoth    sand    dinosaur

6.
 shelter    star    moon

_____ _____ _____
Name   Date   Helper

Science – Say It, Paste It - Initial

Directions: Have the student cut out the pictures at the bottom of the page. The Helper names a picture aloud, then the student glues/tapes or places it on the big picture with the same *beginning* sound.

| Name | Date | Helper |

| solid | machine | living | sand | mixture |
| liquid | seasons | mammoth | balance | location |

#BKCRD-44 *Core Curriculum Vocab Cards Fun Sheets – Level 1* • ©2012 Super Duper® Publications • www.superduperinc.com

Science – Say It, Paste It - Final

Directions: Have the student cut out the pictures at the bottom of the page. The Helper names a picture aloud, then the student glues/tapes or places it on the big picture with the same *ending* sound.

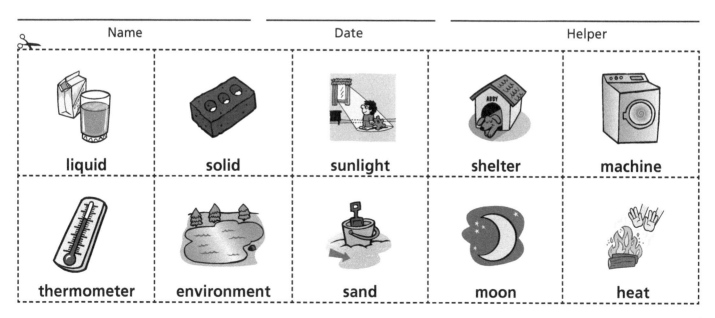

| liquid | solid | sunlight | shelter | machine |
| thermometer | environment | sand | moon | heat |

Science – Breakdown

Directions: Have the student cut out the pictures. The student names each picture aloud and counts how many syllables (or parts of the word) it has. The student glues/tapes or places the picture on the side of the page with that number.

1 syllable	**2** syllables

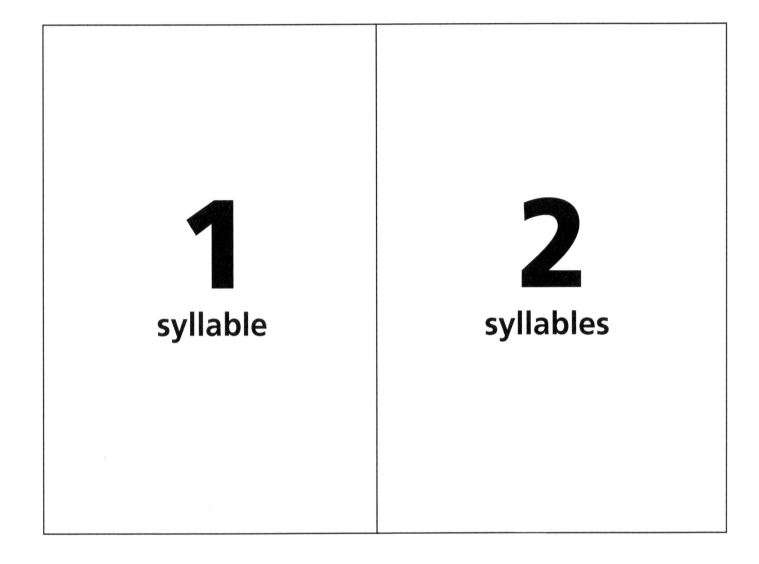

Name	Date	Helper

shelter	balance	sky	star	ocean
freeze	machine	sand	mammoth	heat

#BKCRD-44 *Core Curriculum Vocab Cards Fun Sheets – Level 1* • ©2012 Super Duper® Publications • www.superduperinc.com

Science – Syllable Search

Directions: Have the student cut out the pictures. The student names each picture aloud and counts how many syllables (or parts of the word) it has. The student glues/tapes or places the picture on the side of the page with that number. Have the student find the three words that cannot be used and then tell the number of syllables these words have.

3 **syllables**	**4** **syllables**

_____   _____   _____
Name   Date   Helper

gravity	non-living	dinosaur	environment	location
sunlight	**thermometer**	**mixture**	**balance**	**salt water**

Science – Word Scramble Riddle

Directions: Unscramble the words to name each picture and write the letters in the blanks. Write the letters in circles in order in the blanks at the bottom of the page to answer the riddle.

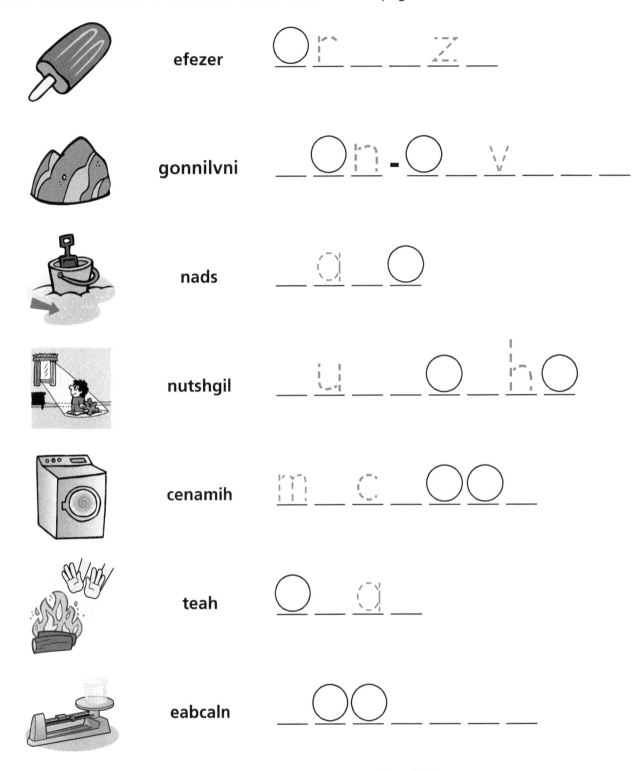

efezer

Ⓞ r __ __ z __

gonnilvni

__ __ Ⓞ n - Ⓞ __ v __ __ __

nads

__ a __ Ⓞ

nutshgil

__ u __ __ Ⓞ __ h Ⓞ

cenamih

m __ c __ Ⓞ Ⓞ __

teah

Ⓞ __ a __

eabcaln

Ⓞ Ⓞ __ __ __ __ __

What's the quickest way to double your money?

__ __ __ __ __ __ __ __ __ __ __ __ f !

#BKCRD-44 Core Curriculum Vocab Cards Fun Sheets – Level 1 • ©2012 Super Duper® Publications • www.superduperinc.com

Science – Word Scramble Riddle

Directions: Unscramble the words to name each picture and write the letters in the blanks. Write the letters in circles in order in the blanks at the bottom of the page to answer the riddle.

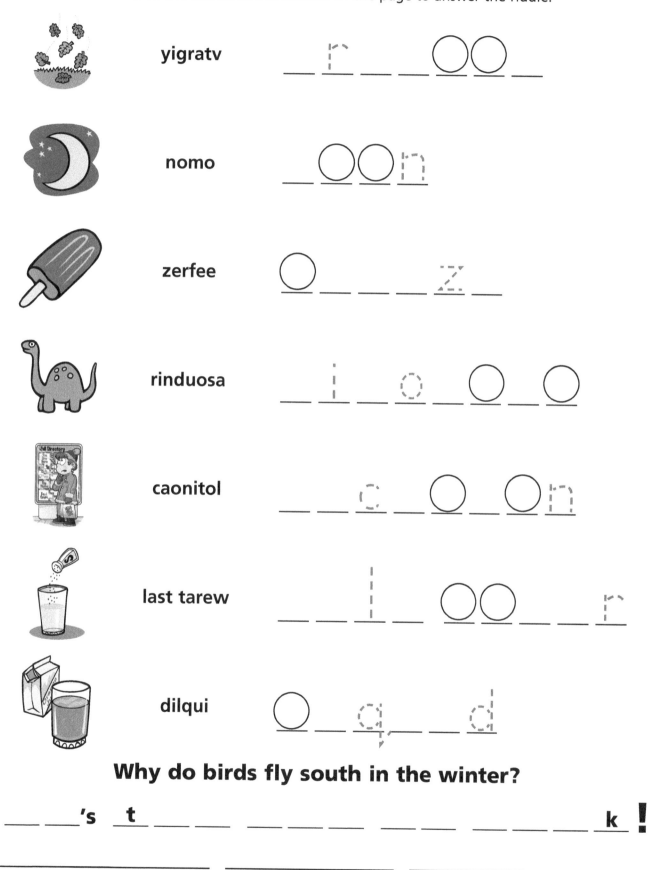

yigratv

nomo

zerfee

rinduosa

caonitol

last tarew

dilqui

Why do birds fly south in the winter?

___ ___'s t ___ ___ ___ ___ ___ ___ ___ ___ ___ ___ k **!**

_____   _____   _____
Name   Date   Helper

Science – Word Scramble Riddle

Directions: Unscramble the words to name each picture and write the letters in the blanks. Write the letters in circles in order in the blanks at the bottom of the page to answer the riddle.

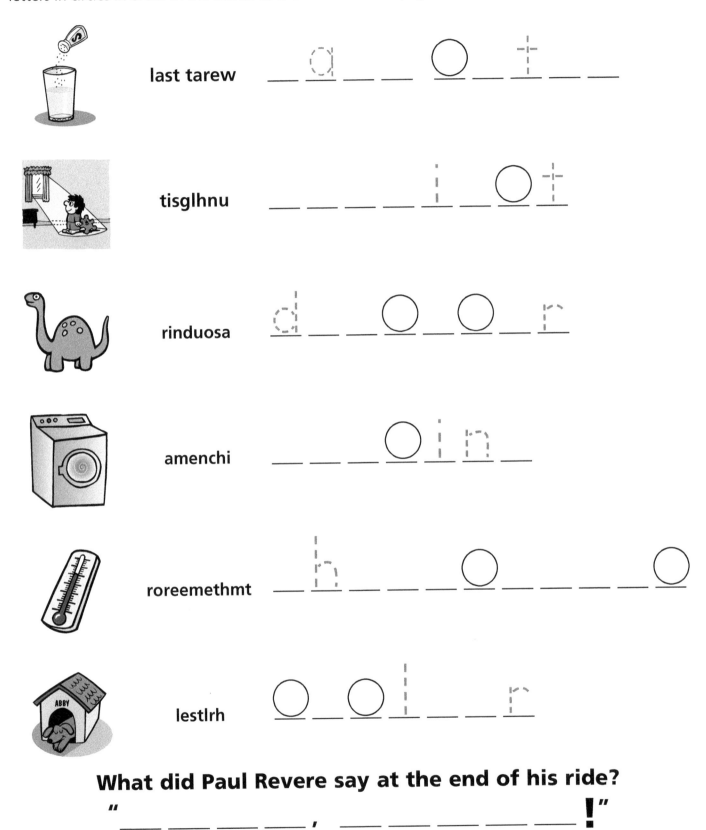

last tarew

tisglhnu

rinduosa

amenchi

roreemethmt

lestlrh

What did Paul Revere say at the end of his ride?

"_____ _____, _____ _____!"

_____ _____ _____
Name　　　　　　　　　Date　　　　　　　　　Helper

74　　#BKCRD-44 *Core Curriculum Vocab Cards Fun Sheets – Level 1* • ©2012 Super Duper® Publications • www.superduperinc.com

Science – Definition Writing

Directions: Read the vocabulary word below each picture. Then, write a sentence beside each picture using the vocabulary word. Use the definition clues at the bottom of the page to help you.

1. environment

2. thermometer

3. salt water

4. dinosaur

5. solid

6. liquid

a state of matter, like water or juice	a mixture of water and salt	a hard state of matter
the land, water, and air around us	a lizard-like animal that lived long ago	a tool to measure how hot or cold something is

Name	Date	Helper

Science – Definition Writing

Directions: Read the vocabulary word below each picture. Then, write a sentence beside each picture using the vocabulary word. Use the definition clues at the bottom of the page to help you.

1. **living**
_____
_____
_____

2. **non-living**
_____
_____
_____

3. **gravity**
_____
_____

4. **location**
_____
_____
_____

5. **mixture**
_____
_____
_____

6. **seasons**
_____
_____
_____

something that breathes and eats	a place where something is	the pull of the Earth making things fall to the ground
winter, spring, summer, and fall	the result of mixing two or more things together	something that does not breathe or eat

Name	Date	Helper

#BKCRD-44 Core Curriculum Vocab Cards Fun Sheets – Level 1 • ©2012 Super Duper® Publications • www.superduperinc.com

Science – Definition Writing

Directions: Read the vocabulary word below each picture. Then, write a sentence beside each picture using the vocabulary word. Use the definition clues at the bottom of the page to help you.

1. **sunlight** _____

2. **machine** _____

3. **heat** _____

4. **moon** _____

5. **sun** _____

6. **star** _____

the object in the sky that heats the Earth	light from the sun	something whose parts can do a job
an object in the night sky that circles the Earth	a bright light that twinkles in the night	to make something warmer

Name _____ Date _____ Helper _____

Science – Definition Writing

Directions: Read the vocabulary word below each picture. Then, write a sentence beside each picture using the vocabulary word. Use the definition clues at the bottom of the page to help you.

1.
   sky
   _____
   _____
   _____

2.
   freeze
   _____
   _____
   _____

3.
   mammoth
   _____
   _____
   _____

4.
   sand
   _____
   _____
   _____

5.
   balance
   _____
   _____
   _____

6.
   shelter
   _____
   _____
   _____

the air above the Earth	a tool used to measure weight	something that protects people or animals from bad weather
used to make castles on the beach	an animal that lived a long time ago and looked like an elephant	to make a liquid hard

_____ _____ _____
Name   Date   Helper

#BKCRD-44 Core Curriculum Vocab Cards Fun Sheets – Level 1 • ©2012 Super Duper® Publications • www.superduperinc.com

Social Studies – Definitions Match-Up

Directions: Draw a line from the definition in Column A to the word that matches it in Column B. Read/Say the definition and its matching vocabulary word aloud.

A

This is a person who lives in a certain country.

This is a period of time that has already happened.

This is a model of the Earth that is round.

This is a period of time that is happening right now.

This is a piece of cloth that represents a country and flies high on a pole.

This is a picture or drawing of a land area.

B

present

map

flag

past

globe

citizen

Name _____   Date _____   Helper _____

Social Studies – Star Match-Up

Directions: Cut out the definitions at the bottom of the page. Shuffle the definitions and place them facedown. Have students take turns reading the definitions and placing them next to the correct pictures. The first player to find the star is the winner.

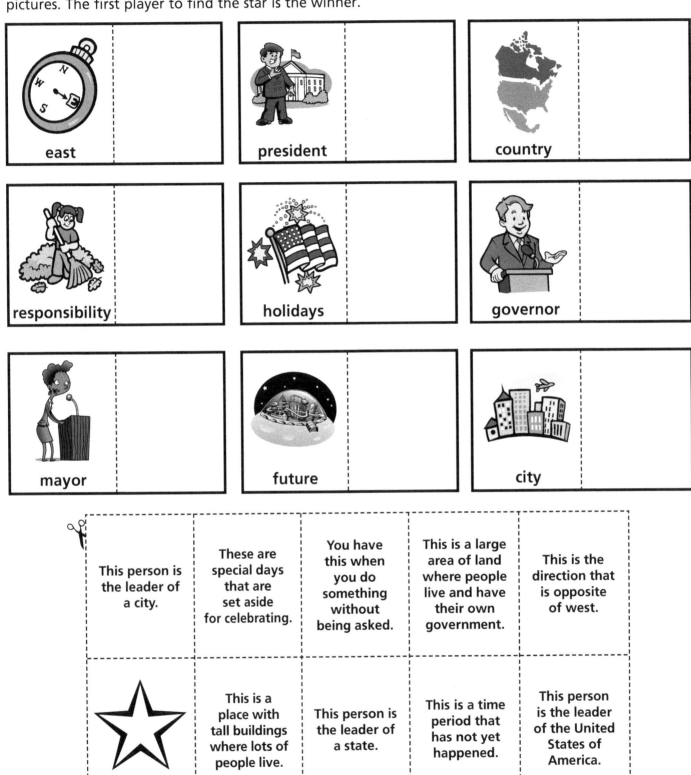

east	president	country
responsibility	holidays	governor
mayor	future	city

This person is the leader of a city.

These are special days that are set aside for celebrating.

You have this when you do something without being asked.

This is a large area of land where people live and have their own government.

This is the direction that is opposite of west.

This is a place with tall buildings where lots of people live.

This person is the leader of a state.

This is a time period that has not yet happened.

This person is the leader of the United States of America.

_____   _____   _____
Name   Date   Helper

#BKCRD-44 *Core Curriculum Vocab Cards Fun Sheets – Level 1* • ©2012 Super Duper® Publications • www.superduperinc.com

Social Studies – Treasure Chest Match-Up

Directions: Cut out the definitions at the bottom of the page. Shuffle the definitions and place them facedown. Have students take turns reading the definitions and placing them next to the correct pictures. The first player to find the treasure chest is the winner.

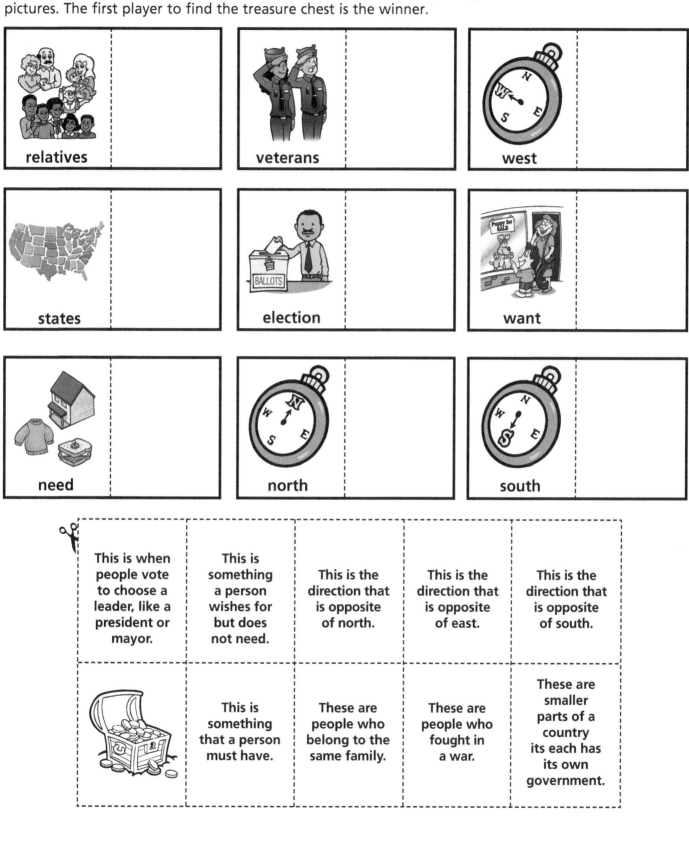

relatives

veterans

west

states

election

want

need

north

south

This is when people vote to choose a leader, like a president or mayor.

This is something a person wishes for but does not need.

This is the direction that is opposite of north.

This is the direction that is opposite of east.

This is the direction that is opposite of south.

This is something that a person must have.

These are people who belong to the same family.

These are people who fought in a war.

These are smaller parts of a country its each has its own government.

Name

Date

Helper

Social Studies – What's the Correct Meaning?

Directions: Read each sentence. Circle the picture and definition on the right that have the correct meaning for the word in bold.

1. Every citizen must obey the **laws** of their country.

These are the rules that people of a country must obey.

This person is the leader of the United States of America.

2. Are Sam and Lucy your **relatives**?

This is a person who lives in a certain country.

These are people who belong to the same family.

3. My father and grandfather are Army **veterans**.

This is a piece of cloth that represents a country and flies high on a pole.

These are people who fought in a war.

4. Cindy lives **west** of the Mississippi River.

This is the direction that is opposite of west.

This is the direction that is opposite of east.

5. There are 50 **states** in the United States.

This is a large area of land where people live and have their own government.

These are smaller parts of a country and each has its own government.

6. There is an **election** for the President of the United States every four years.

This is when people vote to choose a leader, like a president or mayor.

This person is the leader of the United States of America.

_____   _____   _____
Name   Date   Helper

#BKCRD-44 Core Curriculum Vocab Cards Fun Sheets – Level 1 • ©2012 Super Duper® Publications • www.superduperinc.com

Social Studies – What's the Correct Meaning?

Directions: Read each sentence. Circle the picture and definition on the right that have the correct meaning for the word in bold.

1. The **president** of our country lives in the White House.

This person is the leader of a city.

This person is the leader of the United States of America.

2. Canada is a **country** north of the United States.

This is a large area of land where people live and have their own government.

These are smaller parts of a country and each has its own government.

3. Mary's only **responsibility** at home is washing the dishes after dinner.

This is something that a person must have.

You have this when you do something without being asked.

4. Many people take a vacation over the **holidays**.

These are special days that are set aside for celebrating.

This is something a person wishes for but does not need.

5. Ms. Simpson is the first female **mayor** of our city.

This person is the leader of a state.

This person is the leader of a city.

6. I wonder what our city will be like in the **future**.

This is a time period that has not yet happened.

This is a period of time that is happening right now.

_____ _____ _____
Name   Date   Helper

Social Studies – What's the Correct Meaning?

Directions: Read each sentence. Circle the picture and definition on the right that have the correct meaning for the word in bold.

1. All of our relatives live in the same **city**.

This is a place with tall buildings where lots of people live.

This is a large area of land where people live and have their own government.

2. The sun rises in the **east**.

This is the direction that is opposite of east.

This is the direction that is opposite of west.

3. I **want** a new bicycle, but I already have a nice one.

This is something a person wishes for but does not need.

This is something that a person must have.

4. The cold weather came down from the **north**.

This is the direction that is opposite of south.

This is the direction that is opposite of north.

5. Our state's **governor** will serve another four years.

This is a person who lives in a certain country.

This person is the leader of a state.

6. Food is a basic **need** for all people.

This is something a person wishes for but does not need.

This is something that a person must have.

_____ _____ _____
Name   Date   Helper

#BKCRD-44 Core Curriculum Vocab Cards Fun Sheets – Level 1 • ©2012 Super Duper® Publications • www.superduperinc.com

Social Studies – Answer It!

Directions: Read each question. Then, put an X on the letter next to the picture and vocabulary word that best answers the question.

1. Which direction is directly opposite of south?

   A north   **B** east

2. What time is happening now?

   A present   **B** holidays

3. What time has already happened?

   A future   **B** past

4. What do we vote during?

   A election   **B** country

5. Which represents the country of the United States of America?

   A flag   **B** globe

6. Who runs the business of a state's government?

   A president   **B** governor

_____   _____   _____
Name   Date   Helper

Social Studies – Answer It!

Directions: Read each question. Then, put an X on the letter next to the picture and vocabulary word that best answers the question.

1. When is a good time to take vacations?

   (A) holidays   (B) election

2. Who is the leader of a city?

   (A) president   (B) mayor

3. What is something a person must have?

   (A) want   (B) need

4. What object is a model of Earth?

   (A) map   (B) globe

5. Which is a drawing of a land area?

   (A) flag   (B) map

6. Which direction is opposite north?

   (A) east   (B) south

_____ _____ _____
Name   Date   Helper

Social Studies – Answer It!

Directions: Read each question. Then, put an X on the letter next to the picture and vocabulary word that best answers the question.

1. Who is protected by a country's laws?

   (A) laws   (B) citizen

2. Who are the people in your family?

   (A) relatives   (B) veterans

3. Which direction is opposite east?

   (A) north   (B) west

4. What are the smaller areas that a country can be divided into?

   (A) states   (B) country

5. What are the rules citizens must obey?

   (A) responsibility   (B) laws

6. Who is the leader of the United States?

   (A) mayor   (B) president

Name _____   Date _____   Helper _____

Social Studies – Sentence Completion

Directions: Read each sentence below. Complete each sentence using a vocabulary word from the Word/Picture Bank. Write the word in the blank.

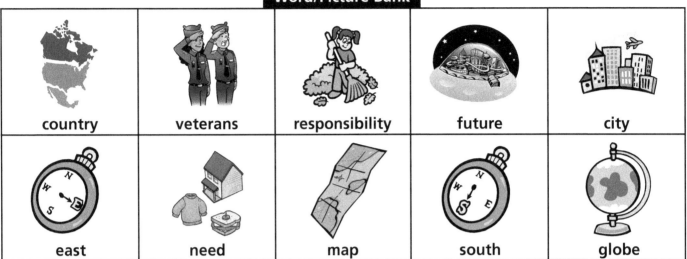

Word/Picture Bank				
country	veterans	responsibility	future	city
east	need	map	south	globe

1. Our city will honor all war _____ at the park on Saturday.

2. This _____ was once a very small town.

3. Maria moved to the United States from a different _____.

4. In the _____, we may be able to visit other planets.

5. We watched the sun rise in the _____ and set in the west.

6. Mom buys what I _____ before she buys what I want.

7. We unfolded the _____ on the table and found our location.

8. A _____ shows us how Earth looks from outer space.

9. It is Jack's _____ to collect items around the house for recycling.

10. Should we go north or _____ to get to the mall?

_____ _____ _____
Name   Date   Helper

#BKCRD-44 Core Curriculum Vocab Cards Fun Sheets – Level 1 • ©2012 Super Duper® Publications • www.superduperinc.com

Social Studies – Sentence Completion

Directions: Read each sentence below. Complete each sentence using a vocabulary word from the Word/Picture Bank. Write the word in the blank.

Word/Picture Bank

holidays	mayor	need	north	present
past	election	flag	governor	citizen

1. Mr. White has been the _____ of our city for 10 years.

2. The _____ for president happens every four years.

3. The are 50 stars on the _____ of the United States.

4. A _____ of the United States can vote at age 18.

5. Our state's _____ will be the guest speaker at the July 4th celebration.

6. Live in the _____, not in the past.

7. Shelter is a basic _____ for everyone.

8. Many people do not have to work on _____.

9. The library has many history books that tell stories of the city's _____.

10. We drove _____ from Florida to Ohio.

_____ _____ _____
Name   Date   Helper

Social Studies – Sentence Completion

Directions: Read each sentence below. Complete each sentence using a vocabulary word from the Word/Picture Bank. Write the word in the blank.

Word/Picture Bank

| relatives | west | states | laws | president |
| citizen | governor | responsibility | veterans | country |

1. Some of our _____ moved here from England.

2. George Washington was the only _____ that never lived in the White House.

3. The _____ of our state visited our new school.

4. It is our _____ as citizens to obey the law.

5. _____ from past wars spoke at the student assembly today.

6. How many of the 50 _____ will elect new governors this year?

7. The United States is a _____ that lies between Canada and Mexico.

8. There are oceans on the east and _____ coasts of the United States.

9. _____ are the rules that people must obey.

10. Can you be a _____ of more than one country?

_____   _____   _____
Name   Date   Helper

#BKCRD-44 Core Curriculum Vocab Cards Fun Sheets – Level 1 • ©2012 Super Duper® Publications • www.superduperinc.com

Social Studies – Which Ones Belong Together?

Directions: Cut out the three pictures in Row 1. Glue the two pictures that go together in the empty boxes on the left. Tell why the two pictures go together. Complete the page one row at a time.

1.

2.

3.

4.

5.

6.

1. past	present	holidays
2. map	flag	globe
3. responsibility	need	want
4. country	relatives	states
5. north	south	veterans
6. president	governor	city

Name _____ Date _____ Helper _____

Social Studies – Which Doesn't Belong?

Directions: Read/Listen carefully to each group of words. Mark an X through the word that doesn't belong. Tell how the other words relate to each other.

1. city, country, flag, states

2. holidays, past, present, future

3. relatives, citizen, veterans, laws

4. president, country, mayor, governor

5. north, west, south, want

6. election, president, laws, north

7. veterans, governor, mayor, present

8. country, past, flag, president

9. map, future, globe, country

10. president, country, city, states

_____ _____ _____
Name   Date   Helper

#BKCRD-44 Core Curriculum Vocab Cards Fun Sheets – Level 1 • ©2012 Super Duper® Publications • www.superduperinc.com

Social Studies – What Doesn't Belong?

Directions: Put an X through the picture in each row that doesn't belong. Tell why the other two pictures belong together.

1.
| east | west | holidays |

2.
| need | flag | want |

3.
| citizen | country | future |

4.
| present | states | past |

5.
| election | globe | map |

6.
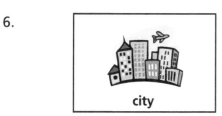  
| city | responsibility | mayor |

_____   _____   _____
Name   Date   Helper

Social Studies – Say It, Paste It - Initial

Directions: Have the student cut out the pictures at the bottom of the page. The Helper names a picture aloud, then the student glues/tapes or places it on the big picture with the same *beginning* sound.

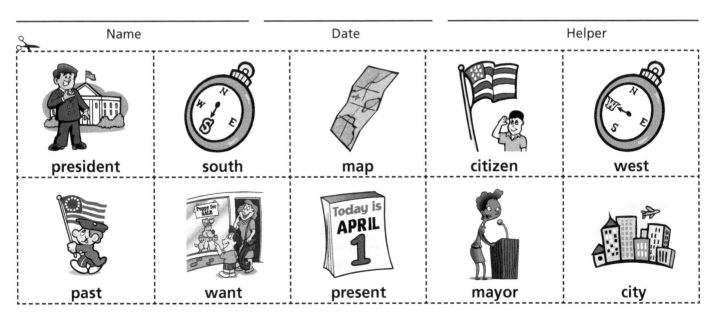

president	south	map	citizen	west
past	want	present	mayor	city

#BKCRD-44 Core Curriculum Vocab Cards Fun Sheets – Level 1 • ©2012 Super Duper® Publications • www.superduperinc.com

Social Studies – Say It, Paste It - Final

Directions: Have the student cut out the pictures at the bottom of the page. The Helper names a picture aloud, then the student glues/tapes or places it on the big picture with the same *ending* sound.

Name   Date   Helper

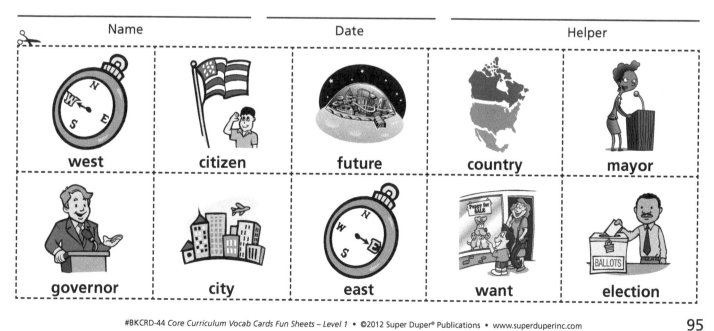

west	citizen	future	country	mayor
governor	city	east	want	election

Social Studies – Breakdown

Directions: Have the student cut out the pictures. The student names each picture aloud and counts how many syllables (or parts of the word) it has. The student glues/tapes or places the picture on the side of the page with that number.

1 syllable	**2** syllables

Name _____ Date _____ Helper _____

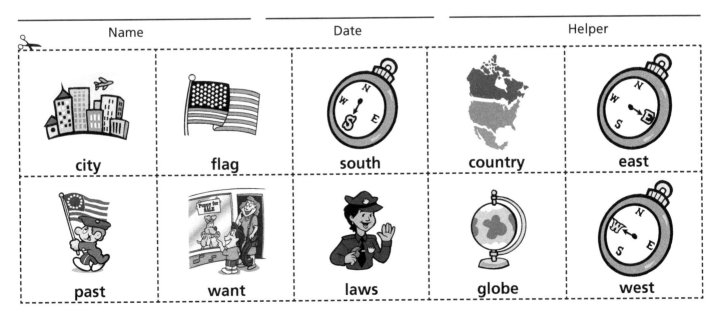

city	flag	south	country	east
past	want	laws	globe	west

 #BKCRD-44 *Core Curriculum Vocab Cards Fun Sheets – Level 1* • ©2012 Super Duper® Publications • www.superduperinc.com

Social Studies – Syllable Search

Directions: Have the student cut out the pictures. The student names each picture aloud and counts how many syllables (or parts of the word) it has. The student glues/tapes or places the picture on the side of the page with that number. Have the student find the word that cannot be used and then tell the number of syllables that word has.

#	2 syllables	3 syllables
	2 syllables	**3** syllables

Name _____   Date _____   Helper _____

present	veterans	citizen	future	mayor
relatives	president	holidays	responsibility	governor

Social Studies – Word Scramble Riddle

Directions: Unscramble the words to name each picture and write the letters in the blanks. Write the letters in circles in order in the blanks at the bottom of the page to answer the riddle.

aflg

⟨◯⟩ __ a __

rlseevtia

__ __ i __ __ ◯ v ◯

yohilsad

◯ __ i __ __ ◯ __ s

husto

◯ __ u __ ◯

ticy

__ ◯ __ y

tpsa

◯ __ ◯ __

What do sea monsters eat?

___ ___ ___ ___ ___nd ___ ___ ___ ___ ___!

Social Studies – Word Scramble Riddle

Directions: Unscramble the words to name each picture and write the letters in the blanks. Write the letters in circles in order in the blanks at the bottom of the page to answer the riddle.

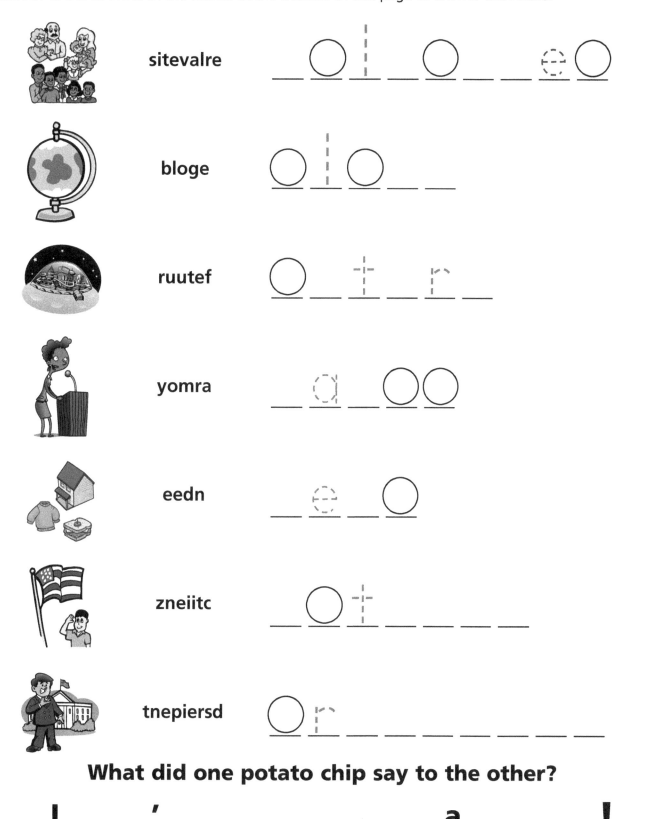

sitevalre

bloge

ruutef

yomra

eedn

zneiitc

tnepiersd

What did one potato chip say to the other?

L __ __ ' __ __ __ __ __ a __ __ __ !

_____   _____   _____
Name   Date   Helper

Social Studies – Word Scramble Riddle

Directions: Unscramble the words to name each picture and write the letters in the blanks. Write the letters in circles in order in the blanks at the bottom of the page to answer the riddle.

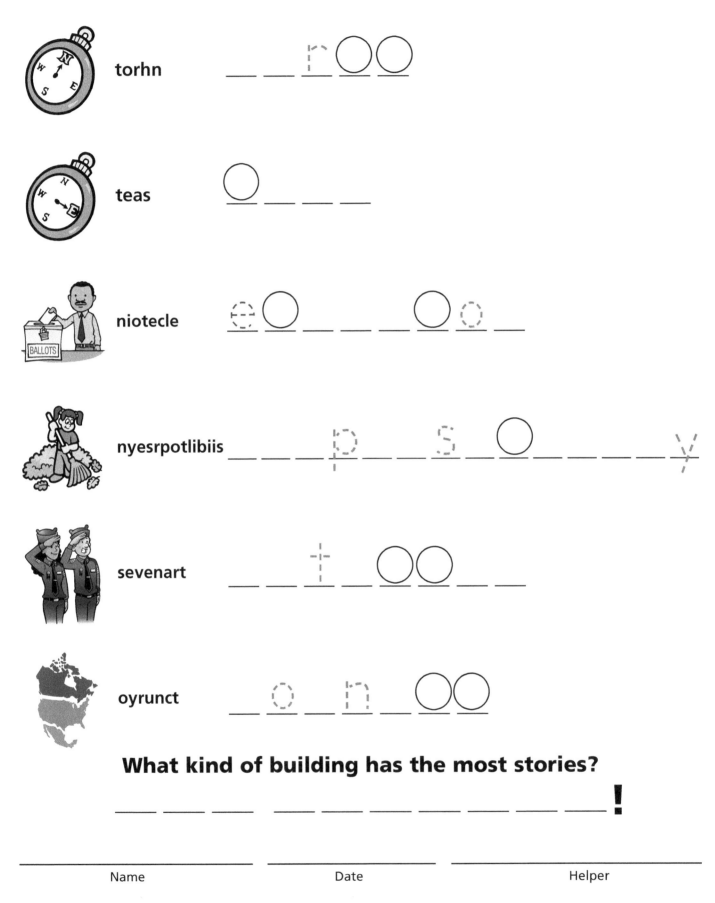

torhn ___ ___ r ◯ ◯

teas ◯ ___ ___ ___

niotecle ◯ ◯ ___ ___ ___ ◯ ___

nyesrpotlibiis ___ ___ ___ p ___ s ◯ ___ ___ ___ ___ y

sevenart ___ ___ t ◯ ◯ ___ ___

oyrunct ___ ◯ ___ n ___ ◯ ◯

What kind of building has the most stories?

___ ___ ___ ___ ___ ___ ___ ___ ___ ___ !

_____ _____ _____
Name   Date   Helper

#BKCRD-44 Core Curriculum Vocab Cards Fun Sheets – Level 1 • ©2012 Super Duper® Publications • www.superduperinc.com

Social Studies – Definition Writing

Directions: Read the vocabulary word below each picture. Then write a sentence beside each picture using the vocabulary word. Use the definition clues at the bottom of the page to help you.

1. holidays

   _____
   _____
   _____

2. responsibility

   _____
   _____
   _____

3. east

   _____
   _____
   _____

4. veterans

   _____
   _____
   _____

5. north

   _____
   _____
   _____

6. country

   _____
   _____
   _____

the direction that is opposite of west	special days that are set aside for celebrating	doing something without being asked
people who fought in a war	the direction that is opposite of south	large land area where people live and have their own government

Name _____ Date _____ Helper _____

Social Studies – Definition Writing

Directions: Read the vocabulary word below each picture. Then write a sentence beside each picture using the vocabulary word. Use the definition clues at the bottom of the page to help you.

1. president _____

2. present _____

3. south _____

4. governor _____

5. west _____

6. map _____

the leader of a state	the direction that is opposite of north	the direction that is opposite of east
the time happening now	a picture or drawing of a land area	the leader of the United States

Name	Date	Helper

#BKCRD-44 Core Curriculum Vocab Cards Fun Sheets – Level 1 • ©2012 Super Duper® Publications • www.superduperinc.com

Social Studies – Definition Writing

Directions: Read the vocabulary word below each picture. Then, write a sentence beside each picture using the vocabulary word. Use the definition clues at the bottom of the page to help you.

1. **want** _____

2. **citizen** _____

3. **election** _____

4. **states** _____

5. **laws** _____

6. **flag** _____

voting to choose a leader	a piece of cloth that represents a country and flies high on a pole	a person who lives in a certain country
smaller parts of a country each having its own government	the rules people must obey	something a person wishes for but does not need

Name	Date	Helper

Social Studies – Definition Writing

Directions: Read the vocabulary word below each picture. Then write a sentence beside each picture using the vocabulary word. Use the definition clues at the bottom of the page to help you.

1. **relatives**

2. **past**

3. **city**

4. **need**

5. **mayor**

6. **globe**

a model of the Earth	people in the same family	a place with tall buildings where lots of people live
a time that has already happened	the leader of a city	something that a person must have

#BKCRD-44 *Core Curriculum Vocab Cards Fun Sheets – Level 1* • ©2012 Super Duper® Publications • www.superduperinc.com

Notes

Notes